W9-DBI-385

GRAMMAR
Form and Function

2B

Workbook

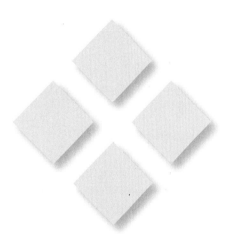

Milada Broukal
Amy Parker

PROPERTY OF

McGraw-Hill
ESL/ELT

ESL 5

Grammar Form and Function 2B

Published by McGraw-Hill ESL/ELT, a business unit of The McGraw-Hill Companies,
Inc., 1221 Avenue of the Americas, New York, NY 10020. Copyright © 2004 by
The McGraw-Hill Companies, Inc. All rights reserved. No part of this publication may be
reproduced or distributed in any form or by any means, or stored in a database or retrieval
system, without the prior written consent of The McGraw-Hill Companies, Inc., including,
but not limited to, in any network or other electronic storage or transmission, or broadcast
for distance learning.

 This book is printed on recycled, acid-free paper containing 10% postconsumer waste.

2 3 4 5 6 7 8 9 QPD 9 8 7 6 5 4

ISBN: 0-07-301380-3

Editorial director: Tina B. Carver
Executive editor: Erik Gundersen
Senior developmental editor: Annie Sullivan
Editorial assistant: Kasey Williamson
Production manager: MaryRose Malley
Cover design: Preface, Inc.
Interior design: Preface, Inc.
Art: Eldon Doty, Preface, Inc.

Photo credits:
All photos are courtesy of Getty Images Royalty-Free Collection.

The McGraw·Hill Companies

Contents

UNIT 10   COMPARATIVE AND SUPERLATIVE FORMS

UNIT 11   THE PASSIVE VOICE

UNIT 12   CONJUNCTIONS AND NOUN CLAUSES

UNIT 8 MODAL AUXILIARIES AND RELATED FORMS

8a *Can, Could,* and *Be Able To* to Express Ability

Student Book 2 p. 194, Student Book 2B p. 2

1 Practice

Write *C* next to the sentence if *can, can't, cannot, could,* or *couldn't* is used correctly. Write *I* if *can, can't, cannot, could,* or *couldn't* is used incorrectly.

_____ **1.** He cans quit smoking.

_____ **2.** Mrs. Lang can't use her computer.

_____ **3.** Bats can hears very well.

_____ **4.** Penguins can't to fly.

_____ **5.** Children can't vote.

_____ **6.** I couldn't sleep well last night.

_____ **7.** I could to stand on my head when I was a child.

_____ **8.** David could ride a bike when he was six years old.

_____ **9.** My wife cannot cook very well.

_____ **10.** Edward can join us tonight.

2 Practice

Kent and Holly are brother and sister. Kent lives in Los Angeles, and Holly lives in New York. Complete the sentences with *can* or *can't*.

Kent: I _____ play tennis outside in January, but you _____.
              1   2

Holly: And you _____ enjoy the snow in Central Park, and you
                                    3

_____ take the subway to work. You have to drive.
              4

Kent: I _____ go to the beach.
              5

Holly: Well, I _____ go to the beach, too!
                            6

3 | Practice

Read about helper monkeys. Complete the sentences with *can* or *can't*.

Capuchin monkeys, like guide dogs for the blind,

_____ improve the quality of life for
            1

quadriplegics (people who _____ use their legs
                              2

or arms). Most families _____ be with their
                             3

loved ones all the time, so these monkeys _____
                                                 4

be very useful because they _____ do many,
                                   5

many things. They _____ help bring food and
                        6

water to people, turn lights off and on, and they _____ pick up things that are
                                                         7

dropped. Many people discover that they _____ work from home with the help
                                               8

of these furry friends.

4 | Practice

Josh was depressed for a while last year. Now he feels much better. Complete the sentences with *could, couldn't, can,* or *can't*.

Last year, I _____ talk to people, and I _____ eat very much.
                   1   2

I felt terrible. I _____ really feel my emotions, and I _____ sleep all
                        3   4

day. Now I feel so much better. I _____ eat, I _____ talk to people,
                                        5   6

and I _____ help other people who are depressed.
            7

5 | Practice

Dennis McClure was very rich, but he lost most of his money when his company went out of business. Complete the sentences with *could, couldn't, can't, can,* or *be able to*. There may be more than one correct answer.

When he had a lot of money, he _____ do anything he wanted. He
                                       1

_____ hire private airplanes, he _____ go to Hawaii for the
      2   3

weekend, and he _____ have parties and invite famous people. When business
                       4

started to go bad, he _____ understand why, and he _____ stop the
                            5   6

decline. He _____ stay in his large house, so he moved into an apartment. Life
                  7

is very different for Dennis now. He _____ travel very much, and sometimes he
                                           8

_____ pay the rent.
      9

6 Practice

Write answers to the questions.

1. What will you be able to do if you speak English well?

   _____.

2. What are you able to do now?

   _____.

3. What can you do if you go to college?

   _____.

4. Can you drive?

   _____.

5. Could you ride a skateboard when you were young?

   _____.

6. Can you cook?

   _____.

8b *May I, Could I,* and *Can I* to Ask for Permission

Student Book 2 p. 199, Student Book 2B p. 7

7 Practice

Identify which people we use *may I, could I,* and *can I* with. Write a, b, or c next to the people. More than one answer is possible.

_____	1. brothers and sisters		**a.**	May I
_____	2. parents		**b.**	Could I
_____	3. close friends		**c.**	Can I
_____	4. teachers			
_____	5. strangers			
_____	6. store clerks			
_____	7. older people			
_____	8. taxi drivers			
_____	9. coworkers			
_____	10. classmates			

8 | Practice

Complete the conversations with *may I, could I,* **or** *can I*. **More than one answer may be possible.**

1. Salesclerk: _____ help you?

    Customer: Yes, I'd like to look at those shoes.

2. You: _____ open a window? It's hot in here.

    Friend: Sure.

3. Friend: _____ borrow your notes? I missed class.

    You: No problem.

4. Teen: _____ borrow the car tonight?

    Dad: Why?

5. Child: _____ have another cookie?

    Mom: Wait until after dinner.

9 | Practice

Write questions with *may I, could I,* **or** *can I.*

1. You want to borrow your sister's favorite CD. Ask her.

    _____?

2. You want to turn on the TV. Your brother is in the room reading a book. Ask your brother.

    _____?

3. You want to come late to class next week because you have a dentist's appointment. Ask your teacher.

    _____?

4. You're at a restaurant and want to order some coffee and a cheese sandwich. Give the server your order.

    _____?

5. Your cell phone's battery is dead, and you need to call your mom. Ask your best friend to use his phone.

_____?

6. You see a father carrying a baby and a big package. He's having trouble opening his car door. Offer to help him.

_____?

7. You are applying to a university and you need a reference from one of your teachers. Ask your English teacher.

_____?

8. You're in a restaurant and you want to smoke. Ask the server.

_____?

9. You just had dinner at your best friend's house. Her roommate made a delicious lemon cake. You want the recipe.

_____?

10. You want to take a photo of your English class. Ask the class.

_____?

8c *Can, Could,* and *Would* to Make Requests
Student Book 2 p. 201, Student Book 2B p. 9

10 Practice

Write requests with *can, could,* and *would*.

1. At the kitchen table, ask your brother to:

   a. pass the salt to you.

   _____?

   b. get you some more water.

   _____?

2. Ask your boss to:

    a. give you some more responsibility at work.

_____?

    b. sign your time sheet.

_____?

3. Ask a stranger on the street to:

    a. tell you where the post office is.

_____?

    b. hold the door to the bank open for you.

_____?

4. Ask a sales clerk to:

    a. tell you how much a coat costs.

_____?

    b. take the price tag off a gift.

_____?

5. Ask your husband to:

    a. make your favorite cake for your birthday.

_____?

    b. give you a ride to the subway.

_____?

6. Ask your teacher to:

   a. give you another example.

   _____?

   b. speak more slowly.

   _____?

7. Ask your grandmother to:

   a. come visit you soon.

   _____?

   b. tell you about when she was young.

   _____?

8. Ask the server to:

   a. bring you the check.

   _____?

   b. ask the people sitting across from you not to smoke.

   _____?

9. Ask your sister to:

   a. turn down the radio.

   _____?

   b. lend you $10.00.

   _____?

10. Before you go on vacation, ask your neighbor to:

   a. take care of your dog, Sammy.

   _____?

   b. pick up your mail.

   _____?

11 Practice

Write *C* next to the sentence if the modal is used correctly. Write *I* if the modal is used incorrectly.

_____ 1. May you help me?

_____ 2. Would you lend me your notes?

_____ 3. Can you come over tonight?

_____ 4. Could I see the photos?

_____ 5. Would I have a glass of water, please?

_____ 6. May I turn on the light?

_____ 7. Can I ask you a question?

_____ 8. May you finish the report today?

_____ 9. Could you put your clothes away?

_____ 10. Would I call you back in a few minutes?

8d *May, Might,* and *Could* to Express Possibility

Student Book 2 p. 204, Student Book 2B p. 12

12 Practice

Identify if the statements and questions refer to ability, permission, request, or possibility.

_____ 1. He might be late.

_____ 2. Laura can help you. She understands the homework.

_____ 3. May I borrow your bike?

_____ 4. She could speak French when she lived in Paris.

_____ 5. Could you repeat the question?

_____ 6. Dale may join us later.

_____ 7. Selena might not be at the library.

_____ 8. Can I go with you?

_____ 9. They could be stuck in traffic.

_____ 10. They can't sing very well.

a. ability

b. permission

c. request

d. possibility

Practice

Complete the sentences with *may, might,* or *could* and your own ideas. More than one answer may be possible.

1. Don't let the baby in the room. She _____ *might fall down* _____ .

2. Phil: What are you getting me for my birthday?

    Pam: It's a surprise.

    Phil: It _____ .

3. That shopping list is long. I (not) _____ enough money.

4. Take your jacket. It _____ tonight.

5. Judy: Do you think you'll pass the test?

    Robert: I don't know. I _____ .

6. Kim: How are you getting to the movie?

    Joy: My dad _____ .

7. Will you wait for me? This (not) _____ very long.

8. Terri: Do you have time to come with us?

    Cathy: I'll check. I _____ .

9. John: Where's the car?

    Eric: I forget where I parked it. It _____ in the garage.

10. Sarah: Where's Ryan?

    Jen: I'm not sure. He _____ .

Practice

Complete the sentences with *may, might,* or *could*.

A. My husband, John, got a job offer in the next town, but we (not, move)

    _____ . We (stay) _____ here, and John (get up)
            1   2

    _____ earlier, or he (work) _____ from home. Of
            3   4

    course, he (not, accept) _____ the position.
                    5

B. Hank is going to Europe and deciding what to take.

I (not, take) _____ my digital camera because I won't have a

computer. I (take) _____ my old film camera. Of course, I (not,

take) _____ any pictures at all. I (send) _____

everyone postcards. I (not, buy) _____ any presents either

because I've been there before.

---

15 **Practice**
Say and write two answers to the questions.

1. What is your best friend doing?

   She/he might be eating dinner _____.

   _____.

2. What do you think your parents are doing?

   _____.

   _____.

3. What do you think you're going to ask for in return for helping a friend study for a big test?

   _____.

   _____.

4. Where do you think you might go on your next vacation?

   _____.

   _____.

5. What could you do after you finish this English course?

   _____.

   _____.

6. What do you think you might do this weekend?

   _____.

   _____.

8e *Maybe* OR *May Be*

Student Book 2 p. 207, Student Book 2B p. 15

16 Practice

Write *C* next to the sentence if *maybe* or *may be* is used correctly. Write *I* if *maybe* or *may be* is used incorrectly.

_____ **1.** We may be late, so start without us.

_____ **2.** It maybe easy for you, but it's not easy for me.

_____ **3.** That may not be a very good idea.

_____ **4.** Maybe Bernie will go with the Smiths.

_____ **5.** May be she went to bed.

_____ **6.** Maybe he'll forget about the money.

_____ **7.** It maybe a surprise party, so don't tell her.

_____ **8.** Jackie may be sorry that she didn't study.

_____ **9.** She may not be home.

_____ **10.** May be I'll study history next year.

17 Practice

Complete the dialogues with *maybe* or *may be*.

1. Warren: I (not) _____ at work tomorrow. _____ I'll win the lottery.

   Sherry: Sure you will. And _____ I'll grow wings and start flying.

2. Alex: I _____ in Hong Kong next week. If so, I'll call you.

   Ling: Great. _____ we can spend a few days together.

3. Frank: Where's Jaime from?

   Tony: I'm not sure. He _____ from Australia, or he _____ from

   New Zealand.

4. Scott: _____ we'll see you at the café.

   Kathy: Yeah. I _____ there around 10:00.

5. I need to lose weight. _____ I'll go to the gym.

6. Gordon: Why don't you feel well?

   Lucy: I _____ allergic to chocolate. _____ I'll call my doctor.

18 Practice
Write sentences about your future with *maybe* or *may be.*

My future job: _____ .

My next vacation: _____ .

Future places to live: _____ .

Hobbies: _____ .

Type of pets: _____ .

Number of future children: _____ .

8f *Let's* and *Why Don't We* to Make Suggestions; *Why Don't You* to Give Advice
Student Book 2 p. 209, Student Book 2B p. 17

19 Practice
Read the situations and offer advice using *why don't you*.

1. My car broke down on the highway this morning, and I don't know what to do.

   Why don't you call your insurance company ?

2. I'm going to be late for class.

   _____ ?

3. Yikes! I overslept!

   _____ ?

4. I've gained five pounds.

   _____ ?

5. My apartment is a mess.

   _____ ?

6. I'm really homesick.

   _____ ?

7. I don't speak English well.

   _____ ?

8. My laptop was stolen!

   _____ ?

Modal Auxiliaries and Related Forms

20 Practice

Complete the suggestions using *why don't we* or *let's*.

1. Kelly: It's 2:00 A.M. in Finland. _____ try calling Janine later.

    Robert: Okay. Hey, what time is it in Tokyo? _____ call Megumi?

2. Calvin: _____ have a party?

    Alan: That's a great idea. _____ invite our class.

    Calvin: Good thinking. _____ call everyone now.

3. Shannon: I'm hungry.

    Danielle: _____ order a pizza.

    Shannon: Okay. _____ ask Steve if he wants some too?

4. Todd: The radio says there's an accident on the highway.

    Alice: _____ take a different route?

    Todd: Okay. _____ get some coffee first.

8g *Should, Ought To,* and *Had Better* to Give Advice
Student Book 2 p. 212, Student Book 2B p. 20

21 Practice

Write *C* next to the sentence if *should, ought to,* or *had better* is used correctly. Write *I* if *should, ought to,* or *had better* is used incorrectly.

_____ 1. You ought to do the job again.

_____ 2. Dave should to call his family today.

_____ 3. We'd better leave soon.

_____ 4. They'd better not to be late.

_____ 5. People shouldn't play video games for very long.

_____ 6. Children shouldn't to eat too many sweets.

_____ 7. I ought to go to the dentist two times a year.

_____ 8. You'd better tell me the truth!

_____ 9. Mark shouldn't buy the vegetables there.

_____ 10. No one should drink the water from that lake.

22 Practice

Complete the *had better* sentences with possible negative results.

1. You'd better not drink so much coffee _____

    or you won't sleep tonight _____.

2. They'd better not cheat on the test _____

    _____.

3. He had better fasten his seatbelt _____

    _____.

4. I'd better lock the door _____

    _____.

5. The students had better turn in the assignments _____

    _____.

6. We'd better not stay up too late _____

    _____.

7. The children had better go to bed now _____

    _____.

8. The little boys had better not play with matches _____

    _____.

9. You'd better not start smoking _____

    _____.

10. I'd better turn down the music _____

    _____.

Modal Auxiliaries and Related Forms

23 Practice

Read the situations and write three sentences with *should*, *shouldn't*, and *had better*.

1. Alec doesn't like his job, so he's often late to work.

   a. *He should look for a new job*   .

   b. *He shouldn't be late to work*   .

   c. *He'd better do something different or he's going to*

      lose his job   .

2. Raul got a job in Chile, but his wife doesn't want to move there.

   a. Raul _____ .

   b. His wife _____ .

   c. _____ .

3. Elena's friend Margo is coming to visit for a week. Elena and Margo sometimes argue.

   a. Elena _____ .

   b. Margo _____ .

   c. _____ .

4. Greta is 14 years old and wants to get her ears pierced. Her mother thinks she's too young.

   a. Greta _____ .

   b. Her mother _____ .

   c. _____ .

5. Brad's having trouble seeing. He is a truck driver.

   a. _____ .

   b. _____ .

   c. _____ .

6. Hans is in love with Anna, but Anna has a boyfriend.

   a. _____ .

   b. _____ .

   c. _____ .

24 Practice

Read the answers and write statements with *should*, *shouldn't*, and *had better*.

1. _If you have a toothache, you'd better call a dentist_ .

   You're right. I'll make an appointment this afternoon.

2. _____ .

   But, I love coffee!

3. _____ .

   Thanks, but I don't really like scary movies.

4. _____ .

   What? You don't like my hair like this?

5. _____ .

   I hate working out!

6. _____ .

   Oh, do you see a police officer?

7. _____ .

   I know. I'll call her tomorrow.

8. _____ .

   Okay, Margo. I won't.

9. _____ .

   I'll get a new one tomorrow.

10. _____ .

    Why not? My parents will never know!

25 Practice

Offer solutions to these problems or situations using *should*, *shouldn't*, or *had better*.

1. What should we do about air pollution? _____

   _____ .

2. What should we do about homelessness? _____

   _____ .

3. What should we do about discrimination? _____

_____.

4. How should people study English? _____

_____.

5. What should we do about the world's overpopulation? _____

_____.

6. What should we do about poverty? _____

_____.

7. What should people do to be happy? _____

_____.

8h *Prefer ... To, Like ... Better Than,* and *Would Rather* to Express Preference

Student Book 2 p. 215, Student Book 2B p. 23

26 Practice

Write *C* next to the sentence if the statement is correct. Write *I* if the statement is incorrect.

_____ **1.** Anita prefers San Francisco than Boston.

_____ **2.** Paul would rather read newspapers than work out.

_____ **3.** Jerry likes summer better than winter.

_____ **4.** Jim would rather work with children than with adults.

_____ **5.** My dad prefers driving than taking the bus.

_____ **6.** Eric would rather meet us at the club to at home.

_____ **7.** Would you rather have the blue one or the green one?

_____ **8.** Crystal prefers short hair to long hair.

_____ **9.** Nana would rather shop in thrift stores than at big department stores.

_____ **10.** Amy likes watching movies to doing laundry.

27 Practice

Read the answers and write questions using *prefer to, like better than,* **or** *would rather.*

1. *Do you prefer sending email to writing letters* ?

   Yes, I prefer sending email.

2. _____ ?

   They'd rather live in the city.

3. _____ ?

   Yes, Martin likes spaghetti better.

4. _____ ?

   No, the class prefers groupwork.

5. _____ ?

   No, she prefers juice.

6. _____ ?

   Jack would rather teach online.

7. _____ ?

   No, Mark likes hip-hop better.

28 Practice

Write sentences with *I'd like* **or** *I prefer.*

1. Why don't we go to the movies?

   (prefer) _____ .

2. Would you like some tea?

   (would like) _____ .

3. Do you like skiing?

   (prefer) _____ .

4. Would you like to be famous?

   (would like) _____ .

5. Would you like to stay here?

   (would like) _____ .

Write sentences about yourself using *prefer to,* *like better than,* or *would rather* and the prompts. There are three different patterns possible.

1. cook   go out to eat

   I'd rather go out to eat than cook.   (OR)

   I like going out to eat better than cooking. (OR)

   I prefer going out to eat to cooking.

2. be outside   watch movies

   _____.

3. cats   dogs

   _____.

4. computer games   sports

   _____.

5. English   history

   _____.

6. rock   rap

   _____.

7. hiking   skateboarding

   _____.

8. videos   DVDs

   _____.

9. (your idea)   (your idea)

   _____.

10. (your idea)   (your idea)

   _____.

30 Practice

Match the questions with the short answers.

_____ **1.** Did your sister have to work last night?

_____ **2.** Does Ryan have to do the dishes?

_____ **3.** Did you have to get gas?

_____ **4.** Did the team have to do it again?

_____ **5.** Do we have to walk there?

_____ **6.** Do I have to go too?

_____ **7.** Did we have to bring something?

a. Yes, we do.

b. No, they didn't.

c. No, he doesn't.

d. Yes, she did.

e. Yes, we did.

f. No, you don't.

g. Yes, I did.

31 Practice

Write sentences about rules in movie theaters using *have to* or *don't have to* and the prompts.

1. turn off cell phones and pagers

    *You have to turn off cell phones and pagers*_____.

2. buy tickets before the movie starts

_____.

3. (not) tip the cashier

_____.

4. be quiet during the film

_____.

5. (not) clap at the end of the film

_____.

6. (not) get dressed up

_____.

32 Practice

Sam has just started a new job as a housekeeper in a large hotel. Here are his responsibilities. Write sentences using *has to* or *doesn't have to*.

1. make beds

    He has to make beds .

2. bring clean towels

    _____ .

3. vacuum

    _____ .

4. (not) deliver food

    _____ .

5. (not) park cars

    _____ .

6. (not) take bags to the rooms

    _____ .

7. be polite to guests

    _____ .

8. check for soap and shampoo

    _____ .

33 Practice

There were a lot of problems at Teddy's high school last year. Read the new rules and write sentences about last year with *didn't have to*.

1. Students must attend 90 percent of all classes to graduate.

2. Students must stay at school during lunch.

3. Students must take an exit test.

4. Students must wear uniforms.

5. Students must read five books over the summer vacation.

6. Students must study a second language.

1. *Last year, students didn't have to attend 90% of all of their classes to graduate* .

2. _____ .

3. _____ .

4. _____ .

5. _____ .

6. _____ .

34 | Practice

Nick is a retired diplomat who is teaching at a university. Write sentences about what Nick had to do when he was a diplomat.

1. think before speaking

   He had to think before speaking .

2. speak other languages

   _____ .

3. love traveling

   _____ .

4. enjoy politics

   _____ .

5. understand cultural differences

   _____ .

6. be sensitive to what people said

   _____ .

7. invite people to his home several times a year

   _____ .

What did your grandparents have to do? Write sentences with *had to* or *didn't have to*.

1. My grandfather had to work six days a week.

2. _____ .

3. _____ .

4. _____ .

Modal Auxiliaries and Related Forms

35 Practice

Underline the most appropriate answers in parentheses.

1. Bert: I ('ve got to / must) eat something.

   Ernie: Me, too. I'm starving.

2. Police officer: You ('ve got to / must) turn off the engine and get out of the car

   slowly with your hands up.

3. Notice in a college catalogue: Students (have got to / must) take LA 100 before they

   take LA 202.

4. I (must / have got to) go. Someone is at my door.

5. Dude, you (must / have got to) see that new movie. The computer effects are awesome!

6. Sign in a restaurant bathroom: Employees (must / have got to) wash hands before

   returning to work.

36 Practice

Write answers to the questions.

1. What do parents have to do?

   _____.

   _____.

2. What do spouses have to do?

   _____.

   _____.

3. What do dancers have to do?

   _____.

   _____.

4. What do pet owners have to do?

   _____.

   _____.

5. What do drivers have to do?

   _____.

   _____.

8j ▶ *Must Not* to Forbid and *Not Have To* to Express Lack of Necessity

Student Book 2 p. 223, Student Book 2B p. 31

37 Practice

Following are things that parents teach their children. Complete the sentences with *must* or *mustn't*.

1. You _____ run with scissors.

2. You _____ point at people.

3. You _____ preheat the oven before you bake cookies.

4. You _____ be careful if you walk home at night.

5. You _____ cut hot peppers and then touch your eyes.

6. You _____ light matches near gasoline.

7. You _____ eat dinner before you have dessert.

8. You _____ call people after 9:00 P.M.

9. You _____ worry so much. Everything will be okay.

38 Practice

Alexander has just gotten a job as a cook. Complete the sentences about the new job with *must, mustn't,* or *doesn't have to*.

1. He _____ use sharp knives.

2. He _____ be late.

3. He _____ serve the food. The restaurant has waiters.

4. He _____ work quickly.

5. He _____ buy the food. The head chef does that.

6. He _____ work well on a team.

7. He _____ have dirty hands.

8. He _____ pick food up off the floor.

9. He _____ collect the money. There is a cashier.

39 Practice

Complete the weight loss guidelines with *must, mustn't,* or *don't have to.*

1. You _____ exercise more.

2. You _____ stop eating completely.

3. You _____ change what you eat.

4. You _____ ask your doctor before you begin losing weight.

5. You _____ be hungry. There are a lot of healthy snacks you can have.

6. You _____ give up!

40 Practice

Read the information about travelers to Finland. Complete the sentences with *must* or *don't have to.*

Travelers _____ have a valid passport. Visitors _____ speak
$\qquad$1$\qquad$2

Finnish because many people speak English. Travelers _____ use travelers'
$\qquad$3

checks because they can use their bankcards in Finland. In the winter, visitors can buy

warm clothes there, so they _____ bring them with them.
$\qquad$4

41 Practice

**Henry is having a surprise party for Karen. Complete the sentences with *mustn't* or
*don't have to.***

Karen is going to be 30! Please come to her surprise party. You _____
$\qquad$1

tell her because it's a surprise! You _____ buy any presents. She doesn't want
$\qquad$2

anything. You _____ bring anything to eat or drink. I'll have everything here.
$\qquad$3

You _____ call me because she might answer the phone. Just email me if you
                4
can come.

Practice

**What do children need to know? Write sentences using *don't have to, have to,*
and *mustn't.***

1. _Children don't have to work._ (OR) _Children have to take naps._

2. _____.

3. _____.

4. _____.

5. _____.

8k *Must* to Make Deductions

Student Book 2 p. 227, Student Book 2B p. 35

43 Practice

**Read the sentences. Decide if *must* means prohibition, necessity, or deduction. Write
the letter of the meaning next to the sentences.**

_____ 1. Paula hasn't eaten since last night. She must be hungry. **a.** prohibition

_____ 2. Dogs must be on a leash. **b.** necessity

_____ 3. Milk must be kept in the refrigerator. **c.** deduction

_____ 4. You mustn't smoke in this restaurant.

_____ 5. Linda has got a new job and has bought a new house.

   She must be making more money.

_____ 6. You mustn't wear jeans to a job interview.

_____ 7. We must water the garden every day in hot weather.

_____ 8. There are two packs of cigarettes in Gordon's truck. He must smoke.

Practice

Write sentences using *must* or *must not* and the following information.

1. Marian ordered chocolate cake and chocolate ice cream.

    She _____.

2. Kyle went to bed early, and he's still there.

    He _____.

3. There are some toys in our new neighbors' yard.

    They _____.

4. The kids ate all the vegetables except for the carrots.

    They _____.

5. Michi doesn't have an email address.

    He _____.

6. Emi hasn't called me back yet.

    She _____.

7. Larry left the city early this morning.

    He _____.

8. I haven't seen a bus in 30 minutes.

    There _____.

9. Baoping just came in, and he's all wet.

    It _____.

10. My watch says it's 10:30, but your watch says it's 10:20. The clock in the lunchroom also says 10:20.

    My watch _____.

81 Imperatives

Student Book 2 p. 229, Student Book 2B p. 37

45 Practice

Rewrite the sentences as imperatives.

1. You shouldn't put metal in the microwave.

   _Don't put metal in the microwave_____.

2. You should shake the bottle before you open it.

   _____.

3. You shouldn't let your dog eat chocolate.

   _____.

4. You should get under the table in an earthquake.

   _____.

5. You shouldn't talk about other people.

   _____.

6. You shouldn't go grocery shopping when you're hungry.

   _____.

7. You shouldn't cut your own hair.

   _____.

46 Practice

Complete the directions for how to do laundry using imperatives and words from the list.

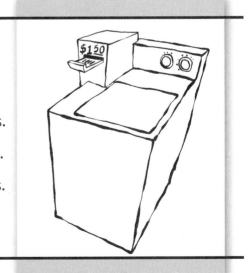

add	don't put in	put
choose	insert	separate

1. _____ the light and dark clothes.

2. _____ the clothes in the washing machine.

3. _____ too many clothes.

4. _____ the water temperature.

5. _____ the soap.

6. _____ coins and start the machine.

47 Practice

Write imperative sentences based on the following situations, words, and your own ideas.

1. What should you do if there's a fire?

   911   elevator   stairs

   a. _Call 911_ _____ .

   b. _____ .

   c. _____ .

   d. (your own idea) _____ .

2. When you're on a roller coaster:

   your seat   hands in the cars   jump up and down

   a. _____ .

   b. _____ .

   c. _____ .

3. If your car has a flat tire:

   side of the road   flashers   spare tire   help

   a. _____ .

   b. _____ .

   c. _____ .

   d. _____ .

4. If you lose your wallet:

   a. _____ .

   b. _____ .

   c. _____ .

5. If you lose your job:

   a. _____ .

   b. _____ .

   c. _____ .

SELF-TEST

A **Choose the best answer, A, B, C, or D, to complete the sentence. Mark your answer by darkening the oval with the same letter.**

1. Mr. Reynolds _____ work anymore. He won the lottery last week!

   A. must   Ⓐ Ⓑ Ⓒ Ⓓ
   B. had to
   C. has to
   D. doesn't have to

2. I _____ vanilla to chocolate.

   A. 'd rather have   Ⓐ Ⓑ Ⓒ Ⓓ
   B. prefer
   C. like
   D. would rather

3. Jesse can't run fast now, but he _____ when he was younger.

   A. could   Ⓐ Ⓑ Ⓒ Ⓓ
   B. must not
   C. might
   D. should

4. _____ you get me some soda, please?

   A. Let's   Ⓐ Ⓑ Ⓒ Ⓓ
   B. Might
   C. Could
   D. May

5. _____ she's home now.

   A. May   Ⓐ Ⓑ Ⓒ Ⓓ
   B. Maybe
   C. Might
   D. Could

6. Yesterday, Mr. Fields _____ go to the hospital.

   A. had to   Ⓐ Ⓑ Ⓒ Ⓓ
   B. must
   C. has got to
   D. might

7. Customers _____ smoke in the restaurant. It's illegal.

   A. have to   Ⓐ Ⓑ Ⓒ Ⓓ
   B. must
   C. don't have
   D. mustn't

8. _____ drink and drive.

   A. Mustn't   Ⓐ Ⓑ Ⓒ Ⓓ
   B. Can't
   C. Don't
   D. Why don't

9. I _____ finish the work. Sorry.

   A. couldn't to   Ⓐ Ⓑ Ⓒ Ⓓ
   B. must to
   C. can't to
   D. wasn't able to

10. Nikki went to bed at 4:00 and got up at 6:00. She _____ exhausted!

    A. doesn't have to be   Ⓐ Ⓑ Ⓒ Ⓓ
    B. must be
    C. mustn't be
    D. can be

B   Find the underlined word or phrase, A, B, C, or D, that is incorrect. Mark your answer by darkening the oval with the same letter.

1. <u>Would</u> you <u>rather</u> <u>stay</u> here <u>than</u> go home?
   A   B   C   D

   Ⓐ Ⓑ Ⓒ Ⓓ

2. <u>Would</u> I <u>help</u> you? Why <u>don't</u> you look at
   A   B   C

   <u>these shoes</u>?
   D

   Ⓐ Ⓑ Ⓒ Ⓓ

3. <u>Why don't</u> <u>be</u> late. You <u>have to</u> <u>be</u> there
   A   B   C   D

   by 5:00.

   Ⓐ Ⓑ Ⓒ Ⓓ

4. We <u>had better</u> <u>blew</u> out the candle, or
   A   B

   there <u>could</u> <u>be</u> a fire.
   C   D

   Ⓐ Ⓑ Ⓒ Ⓓ

5. <u>He</u> <u>likes</u> skiing <u>better</u> <u>to</u> snowboarding.
   A   B   C   D

   Ⓐ Ⓑ Ⓒ Ⓓ

6. Faye <u>could</u> <u>speak</u> Russian fluently in
   A   B

   college. He <u>shouldn't</u> now, but I think
   C

   he <u>must</u> remember a little of it.
   D

   Ⓐ Ⓑ Ⓒ Ⓓ

7. <u>Would</u> I borrow your notes? I had <u>to</u> <u>miss</u>
   A   B   C

   class yesterday because I <u>couldn't</u>
   D

   wake up.

   Ⓐ Ⓑ Ⓒ Ⓓ

8. The lights are off. He <u>doesn't have to</u> be
   A

   home. <u>Let's</u> <u>come</u> back. Or we <u>could</u>
   B   C   D

   call him later.

   Ⓐ Ⓑ Ⓒ Ⓓ

9. <u>May be</u> everyone <u>could</u> come back to my
   A   B

   house. <u>Let's</u> <u>call</u> them.
   C   D

   Ⓐ Ⓑ Ⓒ Ⓓ

10. Please <u>to be</u> <u>quiet</u>. I <u>can't</u> hear what the
    A   B   C   D

    teacher is saying.

    Ⓐ Ⓑ Ⓒ Ⓓ

UNIT 9 GERUNDS AND INFINITIVES

9a Gerund as Subject and Object

Student Book 2 p. 236, Student Book 2B p. 44

1 Practice

Write *G* next to the sentence if the underlined word is a gerund. Write *V* if the underlined word is a verb.

_____ 1. I'm not good at <u>drawing</u>.

_____ 2. The art students are <u>doing</u> research.

_____ 3. <u>Getting</u> a new pet can be fun.

_____ 4. <u>Saying</u> you're sorry isn't enough.

_____ 5. Marilyn is <u>talking</u> to our teacher.

_____ 6. <u>Taking</u> five classes is too much work.

_____ 7. My roommate is <u>taking</u> five classes.

_____ 8. <u>Walking</u> quickly for 30 minutes a day is good for your health.

_____ 9. Holly was <u>walking</u> home when I saw her.

_____ 10. <u>Being</u> an actor is difficult.

_____ 11. <u>Finding</u> parking downtown might not be easy tonight.

_____ 12. <u>Missing</u> more than three classes will seriously affect your grade.

2 Practice

Complete the sentences with gerunds from the list.

being	lying	not worrying	talking
drinking	not having	reading	washing

1. _____ water is good for you.

2. _____ to your children will help them become interested in books.

3. _____ about what other people think is part of growing up.

4. _____ to friends when you're depressed can make you feel better.

5. _____ to your family and friends will get you into trouble.

6. _____ your hair every day can make it dry.

7. _____ a student is fun.

8. _____ a car in this town is a problem.

3 Practice

What are some of your hobbies?

Snowboarding, reading, _____

_____

4 Practice

Complete the sentences with gerunds.

1. I'm good at _____.

2. I'm not good at _____.

3. I dislike _____.

4. I prefer _____ to _____.

5. _____ is dangerous.

9b Verb + Gerund

Student Book 2 p. 238, Student Book 2B p. 46

5 Practice

Underline the correct form of the words in parentheses.

Tim quit (smoke / smoking) last year and started
                  1
(snowboard / snowboarding) and (fish / fishing). He
         2   **3**
goes up north every weekend, but his wife, Josie,

(stays / staying) home because she dislikes (be / being)
      4   **5**
outside. Tim loves (works / working) outdoors. They've
                            6
discussed (moved / moving), but Josie doesn't
                  7
(want / wanting) to. They're postponing (make / making) a
      8   **9**
decision because it hasn't (become / becoming) a big
                                    10
problem yet.

Practice

Rewrite the following sentences. Replace the underlined words with appropriate gerunds. You may have to change the verb.

1. <u>English</u> is interesting.

   Speaking English is interesting. _____ (OR)

   Learning English is interesting. _____

2. <u>Video games</u> can hurt your hands.

   _____.

3. <u>Fruits and vegetables</u> are good for you.

   _____.

4. <u>Money</u> isn't important.

   _____.

5. <u>People</u> can be difficult.

   _____.

6. <u>A new haircut</u> can make you feel great.

   _____.

7. Ingrid can't stand <u>big department stores</u>.

   _____.

8. Horatio doesn't mind <u>housework</u>.

   _____.

9. Yoshimi loves <u>karaoke</u>.

   _____.

7 Practice

Complete the categories.

1. Things you put off:

   a. *doing homework* _____

   b. _____

   c. _____

2. Housework you don't mind:

   a. _____

   b. _____

   c. _____

3. Things you don't want to keep doing:

   a. _____

   b. _____

   c. _____

4. Things you enjoy:

   a. _____

   b. _____

   c. _____

8 Practice

Complete the sentences with gerunds.

1. As a child, I often went _____.

2. Now I often go _____.

3. Next weekend, I'm going _____.

4. When I retire, I'm going to go _____.

5. My mother dislikes _____.

6. She enjoys _____.

7. My country is considering _____.

8. My best friend doesn't mind _____.

9. My classmates are thinking about _____.

9c ◆ Verb + Infinitive

Student Book 2 p. 240, Student Book 2B p. 48

9 | Practice

A famous rock star is taking his record company to court because he believes the company should pay him more money. Read the conversation between two lawyers. Complete the sentences with the infinitive form of the verbs in parentheses.

Lawyer #1: My client has agreed (record) _____

1

five more albums, but before that can happen, he's expecting (receive)

_____ more money.

2

Lawyer #2: Well, my client is refusing (pay) _____ your client. They

3

can't afford (give) _____ him any more money. His last

4

record wasn't very successful.

Lawyer #1: In that case, my client has decided (change) _____

5

record companies.

Lawyer #2: He can't leave yet, because he's promised (make) _____

6

five more albums in his contract. We would prefer (find)

_____ a better solution to this problem.

7

10 | Practice

Read the interview of a famous performance artist. Underline the correct words in parentheses.

Interviewer: Critics disliked your last show.

Artist: I've quit (to worry / worrying) about what critics think.

1

Interviewer: What do you intend (to do / doing) next?

2

Artist: Well, for my next piece I would like (to explore / exploring) new ways of

3

expression. I'm thinking about (to create / creating) using dancers and

4

large sculptures.

Interviewer: How do you get your ideas?

Artist: I refuse (to watch / watching) TV, and I gave up (to read / reading)

5   6

newspapers. This gives me time to focus on my work.

Gerunds and Infinitives

Interviewer: You must enjoy (to work / working).
7

Artist: I can't imagine (to do / doing) anything else. I'll never stop
8
(to make / making) art.
9

☐11 Practice

Complete the sentences with infinitives.

1. I can't afford _____.

2. I can't wait _____.

3. I need _____.

4. I intend _____.

5. My parents would love _____.

6. I'm trying _____.

◆ 9d Verb + Gerund or Infinitive

Student Book 2 p. 242, Student Book 2B p. 50

☐12 Practice

Complete the sentences with gerunds or infinitives.

A. News announcer: The fires have started (spread) _____ to cities
1
close by. Firefighters are continuing (work) _____
2
almost 24 hours a day. It may rain tomorrow. If it begins
(rain) _____, that will help put out the fires.
3

B. Kristen and Dirk are on a blind date:

Kristen: What do you like (do) _____?
1

Dirk: I love (work) _____ in the garden and
2
(go) _____ to movies. How about you? Do you like
3
(be) _____ outside?
4

Kristen: Yes, I do. I like (hike) _____ and
5
(camp) _____ but I dislike (fish) _____.
6   7

C. Judy is at a film, thinking:

This film is so boring. I hate (be) _____ bored. I can't stand
                                            1

(watch) _____ this film for one more minute. I just can't
                  2

continue (stay) _____ in this theater.
                          3

13 Practice

Write C next to the sentence if the gerund or infinitive is used correctly. Write I if the gerund or infinitive is used incorrectly.

_____ **1.** My nephew likes to climb trees.

_____ **2.** He enjoys to play video games.

_____ **3.** He loves watching movies.

_____ **4.** He likes to go to museums.

_____ **5.** He can't stand being cold.

_____ **6.** He can't wait visiting me.

_____ **7.** My brother's family postponed coming here.

_____ **8.** They have a pool, so my nephew wants swimming every day.

_____ **9.** He's just started to take music lessons.

_____ **10.** He would like being a musician when he grows up.

14 Practice

Complete the sentences with gerunds or infinitives.

1. Pilots like _____, but they can't stand _____.

2. Children love _____, but they hate _____.

3. People like _____.

4. Everyone in the world continues _____.

5. Hip-hop music began _____.

Practice

Underline the correct words in parentheses. If both answers are possible, underline both of them.

A. Randy works in a coffee shop. He hates (to get up / getting up) at 5:00 A.M. He
                                                        1

intends (to quit / quitting) soon. He's begun (to look / looking) for a new job. He's
                2   3

been thinking about (to go / going) back to school. He can't wait (to sleep / sleeping)
                              4   5

later in the morning.

B. Mother: Don't forget (to come / coming) straight home after school.
                                                1

Son: Okay, Mom.

Mother: And when you get home, you have to start (to do / doing)
                                                                      2

your homework.

Son: I know.

Mother: I want (to know / knowing) when you get home, so please call me.
                              3

Son: Mom, I promised (to call / calling), so you don't need
                                        4

(to tell / telling) me again.
        5

C. Two teachers are talking about a strict coworker:

Teacher #1:   He needs (to be / being) more patient.
                              1

Teacher #2:   Yes, I agree. He keeps (to say / saying) that the students aren't
                                              2

(to work / working) hard enough.
        3

Teacher #1:   I think he dislikes (to teach / teaching).
                                            4

Teacher #2:   Maybe he just doesn't like (to repeat / repeating) lessons.
                                                    5

D. The company has a new president. She's decided (to close / closing) some of our
                                                              1

offices overseas, but she's not offering (to give / giving) those workers new jobs. Some
                                                  2

of the workers have talked to her, but she's refused (to listen / listening). Some workers
                                                                3

are planning (to strike / striking) because they can't afford (to wait / waiting).
                    4   5

E. My sister and I went (to ski / skiing) and we had a great time! We wanted
                                  1

(to stay / staying) one more day, but I promised my cat sitter that I'd come home on
        2

time. Next year, we'd like (to stay / staying) a full week in the mountains. I can't wait
                                    3

(to go / going) back! I love (to ski / skiing)!
        4   5

16 Practice

Complete the sentences with verbs from the list.

to arrive	to buy	to get	giving	to travel
to be	dancing	getting	to see	yelling

1. Cats dislike _____ their feet wet.

2. We need _____ some money before we go to the restaurant.

3. Sandra can't afford _____ a house yet, but she may have enough

   money next year.

4. You promised _____ at the party early, but you got there

   30 minutes late!

5. He doesn't want to go _____. He's very uncomfortable at clubs.

6. Professor Howard postponed _____ the exam until next week.

7. I'd already apologized, but Ira kept _____ at me.

8. She refused _____ me because she's still angry about what happened.

9. His eyes are closed. He appears _____ asleep.

10. I'd love _____ to China. It's been a dream of mine.

9e Preposition + Gerund

Student Book 2 p. 246, Student Book 2B p. 54

17 Practice

Complete the sentences with the gerund form of the verbs in parentheses.

A. A teacher is talking to the parents of one of his students:

Teddy is capable of (be) _____ an excellent student, but he doesn't care
                              1

about (do) _____ his classwork. He's not interested in (finish)
              2

_____ his assignments, and he insists on (not, follow) _____
    3   4

_____ directions. I'm worried about (pass) _____ him.
                                                      5

B. Archie is thinking about (break) _____ up with his girlfriend, Sylvia. He's
                                        1

worried about (hurt) _____ her, but he believes in (be) _____
                        2   3

honest. He's tired of (pretend) _____ everything is okay.
                                    4

C. Email message from one manager to another:

I'm looking forward to (meet) _____ you at the conference next week. I
                                    1
hope we succeed in (change) _____ management's mind about the new
                                    2
design, but Henry Owens is going to insist on (look) _____ at everything
                                                            3
we decide. If he doesn't approve of (make) _____ these changes, we'll have
                                                    4
to start again.

18 Practice

**Read Belinda's personal ad. Underline the correct form of the words in parentheses.
If both words are possible, underline both.**

I'm interested in (to travel / traveling), and I'm good at (to bike / biking) and
                              1   2
(to swim / swimming). I believe in (to get / getting) to know someone really well. I
        3   4
would like (to meet / meeting) someone who is kind, funny, and intelligent. I look forward
                    5
to (to talk / talking) with you soon.
        6

19 Practice

**Martin, Dan, and Sammy go holiday shopping every year. Read the email message
about their plan to meet, and underline the correct form of the words in parentheses.
If both words are possible, underline both.**

Hi guys,

I'll be glad (to see / seeing) you both. I apologize for not (to contact / contacting) you
                    1   2
sooner, but I've been really busy. Let's plan (to meet / meeting) at 11:00, and I insist on
                                                        3
(to buy / buying) lunch before we start (to shop / shopping). I'm glad about finally
        4   5
(to catch / catching) up with you two.
        6
See you soon,

Martin

20 Practice

Read the sentences and underline the correct prepositions.

1. The families were pleased (in / **of** / about) having someone take care of the children.

2. My great-aunt is fond (in / **of** / about) drinking a cup of tea and having a couple of cookies before bed.

3. I'm tired (in / **of** / about) repeating myself.

4. The engineers are capable (in / **of** / about) improving the technology for the project.

5. Our daughter was interested (**in** / of / about) learning about pottery.

21 Practice

Answer the questions.

1. What was the last thing you apologized for?

   _____.

2. What do you care about doing well?

   _____.

3. What was the last thing you worried about?

   _____.

4. What is something you're capable of doing well, but you don't?

   _____.

5. What was the last thing you succeeded in?

   _____.

9f Infinitive of Purpose

Student Book 2 p. 248, Student Book 2B p. 56

22 Practice

Match the questions with the answers.

_____ 1. Why did you come to Australia?

_____ 2. Why do you work out?

_____ 3. Why did Jen call you?

_____ 4. Why do you save money?

_____ 5. Why do you need a car?

_____ 6. Why are you wearing sunscreen?

_____ 7. Why do you read the newspaper?

a. To get the homework assignment.

b. To prevent sunburn.

c. To stay healthy.

d. To study English.

e. To know what's going on.

f. To go to the store on weekends.

g. To be able to afford to travel.

23 Practice

Answer the questions with *to* or *in order to*.

1. Why do people work?

   _____.

2. Why do people study other languages?

   _____.

3. Why do people drink coffee?

   _____.

4. Why do people go to college?

   _____.

5. Why do people play sports?

   _____.

6. Why do people watch TV?

   _____.

24 Practice

Write C next to the sentence if *to* or *for* is used correctly. Write I if *to* or *for* is used incorrectly.

_____ **1.** He went for buying groceries.

_____ **2.** I'm taking this class for myself.

_____ **3.** We've been invited to Mark's house for dinner.

_____ **4.** Sheila went to the video store to rent some videos.

_____ **5.** Lee's wearing glasses for see better.

_____ **6.** Stephano learned to type for school.

_____ **7.** Frank put your dinner in the oven for keep it warm.

_____ **8.** The children made dinner to us.

_____ **9.** The Kleins need a new truck to new jobs.

_____ **10.** I turned on some music to relax.

25 Practice

Complete the sentences to explain customs or laws in your country.

1. _We go to my grandparents' house, and my mother makes_ _lucky food_ to celebrate New Year's Day.

2. _____ to make a traditional dish.

3. _____ to get a driver's license.

4. _____ to vote in national elections.

5. _____ to enter a good university.

6. _____ to pass my English class.

26 Practice

Complete the sentences with your own ideas.

1. _I bought these new shoes_____ for Saturday night.

2. _____ for their children.

3. _____ a headache.

4. _____ an emergency.

5. _____ for a good time.

9g Adjective + Infinitive

Student Book 2 p. 252, Student Book 2B p. 60

27 Practice

Read the speech from a going-away party. Complete the sentences with the infinitive form of the verbs in parentheses.

I'm happy (see) _____ so many people here tonight. It's difficult
                1

(say) _____ goodbye to so many friends and neighbors. It's difficult
       2

(leave) _____. I was happy (get) _____ a better job, but
       3   4

I'm sorry (be) _____ moving so far away.
           5

28 Practice

Jae is talking to his friends about his English class. Complete the sentences with the infinitive form of the verbs in parentheses.

I was surprised (learn) _____ we have to give presentations in class. I'm
                1

afraid (speak) _____ in public. It's difficult (not, be)
            2

_____ nervous. I was happy (hear) _____ my classmates feel
   3   4

the same way. When I speak in front of people, it's easy (forget) _____
                                     5

my topic. Our teacher was sorry (hear) _____ that we are nervous about
                         6

presentations.

29 Practice

A professor is meeting with Rachel. Complete the sentences with the infinitive form of the verbs in parentheses.

I'm pleased (inform) _____ you
                            1
that you have enough credits to pass the course
this semester. I was surprised (discover)

_____ you changed the topic of your final presentation at the last minute,
        2
but am very happy (know) _____ that you still finished your coursework on
                                 3
time. I'm always glad (give) _____ students good news.
                                    4

30 Practice

Rewrite the sentences using gerunds.

1. It's scary to be in a car accident.

   _Being in a car accident is scary_____.

2. It's difficult not to have a job.

   _____.

3. It's important to brush your teeth.

   _____.

4. It's exciting to ride roller coasters.

   _____.

5. It's fun to make cookies.

   _____.

6. It's polite to say *please* and *thank you*.

   _____.

7. It's exciting to play soccer.

   _____.

8. It can be dangerous to walk home alone at night.

   _____.

9h Enough and Too with Adjectives and Adverbs; Enough and Too with Infinitives; Enough with Nouns

Student Book 2 p. 254, Student Book 2B p. 62

31 Practice

Write C next to the sentence if *too* or *enough* is used correctly. Write *I* if *too* or *enough* is used incorrectly.

_____ **1.** I'm not enough tall to reach the shelf.

_____ **2.** Kimberly doesn't have enough time to finish.

_____ **3.** Steve feels too sad to talk to anyone.

_____ **4.** It's enough warm to work out.

_____ **5.** Is there enough money for rent?

_____ **6.** It's cold enough to drink hot chocolate.

_____ **7.** He's not enough old to go there alone.

_____ **8.** We're not enough rich to buy a new car.

_____ **9.** They're too hungry to think clearly.

_____ **10.** The sofa is too heavy to carry.

32 Practice

Complete the sentences with *too* or *enough*.

1. He's _____ sick to go to school.

2. Lucy doesn't feel well _____ to get up.

3. We can't go. We're _____ tired.

4. You're _____ close to the edge. Be careful!

5. My son isn't tall _____ to ride the roller coaster.

6. It's _____ dark to see. Let's turn around.

7. Do they have _____ time to stop at home first?

8. I had _____ corn for dinner.

33 Practice

Complete the sentences with your own ideas.

1. It's not _____ enough to _____.

2. It's too _____ to _____.

3. I'm too _____ to _____.

4. I'm not _____ enough to _____.

5. I have enough _____ to _____ but I don't have

   enough _____ to _____.

6. My parents are _____ enough to _____

   but they are too _____ to _____.

9i *Be Used To* + Gerund and *Be Accustomed To* + Gerund

Student Book 2 p. 256, Student Book 2B p. 64

34 Practice

Jeremy graduated from college last year and has been working for a large company for six months. Complete the sentences about what he's used to with the verbs in parentheses.

1. When I first started working, I wasn't used to (get up) _____

   early.

2. I wasn't used to (wear) _____ suits every day and

   (work) _____ long hours.

3. I'm getting used to (be) _____ a professional.

4. I've gotten used to (be) _____ called 'Mr. Jackson', instead of

   'Jeremy'.

5. I'm still not used to (have) _____ an assistant.

6. It is easy to get used to (make) _____ more money!

7. I like my job, and I'm excited about (go) _____ to work every day.

Practice

Write *C* next to the sentence if *be used to* or *be accustomed to* is used correctly. Write *I* if *be used to* or *be accustomed to* is used incorrectly.

_____ **1.** We're used to working hard.

_____ **2.** She used to eating healthy food.

_____ **3.** Mikhail is getting used to driving in city traffic.

_____ **4.** I'm not used to get up so early.

_____ **5.** My uncle use to drinking a lot of coffee.

_____ **6.** My boss isn't accustomed to people disagreeing with her.

_____ **7.** She use to being admired for her photography.

_____ **8.** I'm not accustomed to stay up late.

_____ **9.** I'm not used to speaking English all the time.

_____ **10.** Liz is used to be heavier.

| 36 | Practice

Complete the sentences with phrases from the list or your own ideas. Be sure to use the gerund form.

eat different types of food	photographers take photos of his house
fans cheer for her	students be late to class
people ask for his autograph	students discuss their courses

1. The teacher isn't accustomed to _____.

2. The actor is used to _____.

3. The student advisor is used to _____.

4. Sally travels to many countries. She is used to _____.

5. The soccer player is used to _____.

6. The famous architect is accustomed to _____.

| 37 | Practice

What are you used to doing? Write sentences about yourself and your friends.

1. _I'm used to working all day_ _____.

2. _____.

3. _____.

9j   *Be Supposed* + Infinitive

Student Book 2 p. 258, Student Book 2B p. 66

38 | Practice

These are the rules for English class. Complete the sentences with *be supposed to* or *be not supposed to*.

1. be late

   We're not supposed to be late _____ .

2. work in groups

   _____ .

3. study for quizzes

   _____ .

4. prepare presentations

   _____ .

5. write three essays

   _____ .

6. turn in homework late

   _____ .

7. eat lunch in class

   _____ .

8. buy the textbook

   _____ .

9. bring our book to class every day

   _____ .

10. chew gum when we speak

    _____ .

39 Practice

Sherry is showing Pierre how to use the bus. Complete the sentences with the correct form of *be supposed to* or *be not supposed to*.

Pierre: What (do) _____ ?
                                1

Sherry: You (put) _____ money in the machine.
                            2

Pierre: Then what?

Sherry: Then, you (take) _____ a transfer. You
                                 3

(move) _____ to the back of the bus. You
              4

(sit) _____ in the front seats. Those are for seniors.
          5

Pierre: Okay.

Sherry: You (talk) _____ to the bus driver because he or she is
                          6

busy. And you (eat or drink) _____ on the bus.
                                        7

40 Practice

It's Halloween in the United States. David is explaining to Yutaka what they are supposed to do. Complete the sentences with *be supposed to* or *be not supposed to*.

David: We (get) _____ pumpkins and
                        1

(buy) _____ some candy.
            2

Yutaka: What (we, do) _____ with the candy?
                              3

David: Everyone (dress) _____ in a costume. Small children are going
                                4

to come to our house, and we (give) _____ them some candy.
                                                5

Yutaka: Sounds like fun!

41 Practice

What are some responsibilities at home and at school? Write sentences with *be supposed to* or *be not supposed to*.

1. *My brother is supposed to take out the garbage*. (OR)

   Our class is supposed to finish this unit tomorrow.

2. _____ .

3. _____ .

A **Choose the best answer, A, B, C, or D, to complete the sentence. Mark your answer by darkening the oval with the same letter.**

1. _____ stamps is one of my hobbies.

    A. Collect   Ⓐ Ⓑ Ⓒ Ⓓ
    B. To collecting
    C. For collect
    D. Collecting

2. Cami's grandfather enjoyed _____ golf.

    A. to play   Ⓐ Ⓑ Ⓒ Ⓓ
    B. playing
    C. play
    D. to playing

3. The detective intends _____ what happened.

    A. to find out   Ⓐ Ⓑ Ⓒ Ⓓ
    B. finding out
    C. find out
    D. to finding out

4. James _____ doing his homework.

    A. intends   Ⓐ Ⓑ Ⓒ Ⓓ
    B. would like
    C. likes
    D. plans to

5. The women believe _____ finishing the project.

    A. about   Ⓐ Ⓑ Ⓒ Ⓓ
    B. on
    C. of
    D. in

6. Toni came over _____ the situation.

    A. to discuss   Ⓐ Ⓑ Ⓒ Ⓓ
    B. for discuss
    C. discussing
    D. discuss

7. My little brother is afraid _____ in the dark.

    A. sleep   Ⓐ Ⓑ Ⓒ Ⓓ
    B. of sleeping
    C. for sleep
    D. sleeping

8. Cathy's too relaxed _____ .

    A. enough   Ⓐ Ⓑ Ⓒ Ⓓ
    B. studying
    C. study
    D. to study

9. Dad was supposed _____ the VCR for 9:00.

    A. too set   Ⓐ Ⓑ Ⓒ Ⓓ
    B. set enough
    C. to set
    D. set

10. Maybelle isn't used _____ up so early.

    A. to getting   Ⓐ Ⓑ Ⓒ Ⓓ
    B. getting
    C. to get
    D. get

B **Find the underlined word or phrase, A, B, C, or D, that is incorrect. Mark your answer by darkening the oval with the same letter.**

1. To travel is exciting. I enjoy meeting
      A   B   C   D

   people from other countries.

   Ⓐ Ⓑ Ⓒ Ⓓ

2. He's decided to give up to smoke.
      A   B   C   D

   Ⓐ Ⓑ Ⓒ Ⓓ

3. Our team decided to ask for more
            A   B C

   time, but Mr. Roberts refused agree.
                           D

   Ⓐ Ⓑ Ⓒ Ⓓ

4. Chuck apologized to being late. He
         A   B

   couldn't afford to take a taxi.
        C   D

   Ⓐ Ⓑ Ⓒ Ⓓ

5. We stopped get some vegetables
      A   B

   for dinner.
    C   D

   Ⓐ Ⓑ Ⓒ Ⓓ

6. Sam doesn't want to come with us.
         A   B

   He's afraid of drive in the city.
      C   D

   Ⓐ Ⓑ Ⓒ Ⓓ

7. Renata hates wait for the bus.
        A   B C

   She's too impatient.
      D

   Ⓐ Ⓑ Ⓒ Ⓓ

8. We don't have enough time to finish the
           A   B

   test. It's enough difficult to do.
        C   D

   Ⓐ Ⓑ Ⓒ Ⓓ

9. People here used to tipping 15% at
          A   B

   restaurants when they finish eating.
                 C   D

   Ⓐ Ⓑ Ⓒ Ⓓ

10. I can't talk now. I need to leave.
                 A   B

    I was supposed to being there
            C   D

    15 minutes ago.

    Ⓐ Ⓑ Ⓒ Ⓓ

UNIT 10 COMPARATIVE AND SUPERLATIVE FORMS

10a Adjectives and Adverbs

Student Book 2 p. 264, Student Book 2B p. 72

1 Practice

Read about rattlesnakes. Underline the correct form of the words in parentheses.

Rattlesnakes are (poisonous / poisonously),
1
but not many people die from their bites. They

like (hot / hotly), (dry / dryly) places. They move
2   **3**
(quick / quickly) but don't see (good / well).
4   **5**
They can be from two feet to eight feet

(long / longly). Some rattlesnakes are
6
(endangered / endangeredly).
7

2 Practice

Ruth had trouble sleeping last night. Underline the correct form of the words in parentheses.

1. The upstairs neighbor was playing his stereo (loud / loudly) very late last night.

2. The city buses were driving (noisy / noisily) past her apartment.

3. Ruth was (hungry / hungrily) when she went to bed.

4. She has been (tired / tiredly) a lot lately.

5. She's not been sleeping (good / well).

6. But she has been very (happy / happily).

Practice

If the sentence has an adjective, underline it. If the sentence has an adverb, circle it.

1. Chad has just bought a large house.

2. My neighborhood is noisy.

3. Margaret and Kit work well together.

4. We got dressed quickly.

5. Cheetahs move fast.

6. The laptop is expensive.

7. He speaks seriously.

10b Participles as Adjectives

Student Book 2 p. 266, Student Book 2B p. 74

4 **Practice**

Underline the correct words in parentheses.

1. The exhibit was (fascinated / fascinating).

2. We were (fascinated / fascinating) by the exhibit.

3. It was (interested / interesting) to see the photos from World War II.

4. My brother was (interested / interesting) in the photos from Europe.

5. We were (annoyed / annoying) because the bus was late.

6. It was (annoyed / annoying) to wait so long.

7. We were (bored / boring) on the way home.

8. The plane trip was (bored / boring). It was too long.

9. I was (surprised / surprising) to see Kendra.

10. It was (surprised / surprising) to see Kendra there.

Practice

Read the sentences. Then complete the sentences with participle adjectives.

1. The loud noise frightened the animals.

   a. The animals were _frightened_ .

   b. The noise was _frightening_ .

2. The trip excited us.

   a. We were _____ .

   b. The trip was _____ .

3. The stories amused our son.

   a. The stories were _____ .

   b. Our son was _____ .

4. The movie bored the class.

   a. The class was _____ .

   b. The movie was _____ .

5. My job tired me.

   a. My job is _____ .

   b. I'm _____ .

6. The cruise relaxed my parents.

   a. My parents were _____ .

   b. The cruise was _____ .

7. The new car surprised Sally's husband.

   a. The new car was _____ .

   b. Sally's husband was _____ .

6 | Practice

Write _C_ next to the sentence if the adjective is used correctly. Write _I_ if the adjective is used incorrectly.

_____ 1. The movie was frightened.

_____ 2. The weekend was relaxing.

_____ 3. We weren't amusing at her joke.

_____ 4. The children were so excited that they didn't sleep.

_____ 5. Bruce was really surprised.

_____ 6. The pool was relaxed.

_____ 7. We were irritating by the noise.

_____ 8. The computer game was annoyed.

_____ 9. Biology is bored.

_____ 10. Patricia was interested in the lecture.

7 | Practice

Complete the sentences with your own ideas.

1. _____ is frightening.

2. _____ is boring.

3. _____ is interesting.

4. _____ is amusing.

5. _____ is exciting.

6. My best friend is _____.

7. My hobbies are _____.

8. _____ tired.

9. _____ relaxed.

10. I'm _____.

10c Adjectives After Verbs

Student Book 2 p. 269, Student Book 2B p. 77

8 Practice

Complete the sentences with adjectives.

1. This restaurant looks _____.

2. Mmm. It smells _____ in here.

3. Everyone seems _____.

4. I am getting _____!

5. Everything looks _____.

6. This bread tastes _____.

9 Practice

Yesterday, we walked through a rose garden. Underline the correct form of the words in parentheses.

The garden looked (beautiful / beautifully). The roses smelled (sweet / sweetly), and we
₁

felt (good / well). It seemed so (peaceful / peacefully). We walked (slow / slowly) and
₃   ₄   ₅

looked (careful / carefully) at everything. We had a picnic, and everything tasted
₆

(great / greatly). After two hours, we got (tired / tiredly), and we were a little
₇   ₈

(sad / sadly) to leave.
₉

10 Practice

Complete the sentences with an appropriate verb.

1. I _____ carefully.

2. I _____ good.

3. I _____ well.

4. I _____ quickly.

5. My parents _____ nicely.

6. My best friend _____ easily.

7. My class _____ intelligent.

8. My country's food _____ delicious.

10d *As + Adjective + As; As + Adverb + As*

Student Book 2 p. 271, Student Book 2B p. 79

11 Practice

Write sentences with *as ... as* or *not as ... as* about life in the 1950s and now. Use words from the list or your own ideas.

advanced	efficient	popular	small
amazing	good/bad	powerful	sophisticated

1. cars

    In the 1950s, cars weren't as efficient as they are now .

2. computers

    _____.

3. stereos

    _____.

4. music

    _____.

5. science

    _____.

6. movie effects

_____.

7. apartments

_____.

8. TVs

_____.

12 | Practice

Paula is talking about the differences between her small corner market and the large grocery store across town. Complete the sentences with _(be) not as ... as._

1. The prices at the grocery store (high) _aren't as high as_ prices at the

corner market.

2. Shopping at the grocery store (convenient) _____

shopping at the corner market.

3. The people working at the grocery store (friendly) _____

the people working at the corner market.

4. Fruits and vegetables at the grocery store (fresh) _____

they are at the corner market.

5. Choices at the corner market (varied) _____ choices

at the grocery store.

6. The grocery store _____ open (late) _____

the corner market is.

7. The lighting in the corner market

(bright) _____

the lighting in the grocery store.

8. Shopping at the grocery store

(nice) _____

shopping at the corner market.

Comparative and Superlative Forms

13 Practice

Complete the sentences with your own ideas.

1. _____ isn't as difficult as

_____.

2. _____ is as interesting as

_____.

3. _____ tastes as good as

_____.

4. _____ works as quickly as

_____.

5. _____ isn't as fun as

_____.

6. My mother is as _____ as my father.

7. My father isn't as _____ as my mother.

8. My bedroom isn't as _____ as the living room.

9. Today is as _____ as yesterday.

10. My friends are as _____ as I am.

11. I'm not as old as _____.

12. I'm as intelligent as _____.

13. I'm not as shy as _____.

10e Comparative Forms of Adjectives and Adverbs

Student Book 2 p. 274, Student Book 2B p. 82

14 Practice

Complete the chart. If there is more than one possibility, write them both.

Adjective or Adverb	Comparative Form
1. thin	thinner than
2. clean	
3.	lazier than
4. expensive	

Adjective or Adverb	Comparative Form
5.	earlier than
6. bright	
7.	better than
8.	more amusing than
9. quiet	
10. dirty	
11. badly	
12.	further than
13. well	
14.	more tolerant than
15. expensive	
16.	more beautifully than
17.	worse than
18. polite	
19. quietly	
20. sophisticated	

15 Practice

Write _C_ next to the sentence if the comparative form of the adjective is used correctly. Write _I_ if the comparative form of the adjective is used incorrectly.

_____ **1.** My mother's shoes are bigger than mine.

_____ **2.** Lunch was less good than dinner.

_____ **3.** English is less interesting than mathematics.

_____ **4.** I'm not as young as I used to be.

_____ **5.** Angela seems happier than she was a year ago.

_____ **6.** The new curtains are more longer than the old ones.

_____ **7.** The sun isn't as bright as it was yesterday.

_____ **8.** The homework was more difficult than the test.

_____ **9.** The room feels less colder than it was this morning.

_____ **10.** Ken got to school later than usual.

Comparative and Superlative Forms

16 Practice

Three musicians from a band are talking about what they need to do before they go on tour. Complete the conversation with the comparative form of the adjectives or adverbs in parentheses.

Sam: I think I should get a (short) _____ haircut _____
       $\underset{1}{}$ $\underset{(1)}{}$
       the one I have now.

Allison: Well if you do, then I'll dye my hair a (bright) _____ color
           $\underset{2}{}$
           _____ it is.
           $\underset{(2)}{}$

Leslie: Cool. And I should buy a (good) _____ violin _____ the
          $\underset{3}{}$ $\underset{(3)}{}$
          one I play now.

Allison: Well, we definitely need a (reliable) _____ van
           $\underset{4}{}$
           _____ the one we drive now.
           $\underset{(4)}{}$

Sam: Do you think we should learn a few (interesting) _____
       $\underset{5}{}$
       songs _____ the ones we play now?
             $\underset{(5)}{}$

Leslie: As long as we have enough time. I want to feel (comfortable) _____
          $\underset{6}{}$
          _____ onstage _____ the last tour.
                                     $\underset{(6)}{}$

17 Practice

Matthew and Ellison have moved from the Bahamas to London, and their lives are very different now. Complete the sentences with the comparative form of the adjective or adverb and *than* if necessary.

1. London is much (cold) _____

   the islands.

2. The city is (crowded) _____

   our old neighborhood, and the apartments are (big) _____.

3. Life was (slow) _____ in the Caribbean.

4. It was also (exciting) _____ living in the tropics.

5. The schools are (challenge) _____ the ones in the Bahamas.

6. I think things in the Bahamas were a little (expensive) _____

in London.

7. Our neighborhood in London is (noisy) _____.

8. We are (busy) _____ we were in Nassau, but we're getting used to it.

9. Matthew is (happy) _____ he was in the Bahamas, but Ellison

feels (depressed) _____ he did there.

18 Practice

Complete the sentences comparing talking on the phone with sending email.

1. Talking on the phone is ___*more expensive than*___ sending email,

especially to friends overseas.

2. Talking on the phone is _____ sending email.

3. Sending email is _____ talking on the phone.

4. Sending email is _____ talking on the phone.

5. _____.

6. _____.

19 Practice

Rewrite the following sentences to have the same meaning using comparative forms. Change the pronouns if necessary.

1. His last movie wasn't as funny as his first movie was.

___*His first movie was funnier than his last movie*___.

2. My sister isn't as lazy as my brother is.

_____.

3. David doesn't play violin as well as Miriam does.

_____.

4. Watching TV isn't as interesting as playing video games.

_____.

5. Arthur doesn't work as quickly as George does.

_____.

6. Heather isn't as nice as Theresa is.

_____.

7. That old operating system isn't as fast as the new one is.

_____.

8. Tokyo isn't as far as Beijing is.

_____.

9. The doctor's appointment wasn't as bad as I thought it was going to be.

_____.

10. This exercise isn't as easy as the first one was.

_____.

10f Superlative Forms of Adjectives and Adverbs
Student Book 2 p. 280, Student Book 2B p. 88

20 Practice

Write _C_ next to the sentence if the superlative form of the adjective is used correctly. Write _I_ if the superlative form of the adjective is used incorrectly.

_____ **1.** What was the most exciting winter event last year?

_____ **2.** The day our son Sidney was born was the more exciting day of my life.

_____ **3.** Last winter was the most cold in my memory.

_____ **4.** The last month before the baby was born was the most difficult one of all.

_____ **5.** We celebrated the new baby's birth at _Paolina_, the best restaurant in the city.

_____ **6.** It was the most wonderful party ever.

_____ **7.** That party was the most large party we'd ever had.

_____ **8.** I bought that baby crib because it was the cheaper.

_____ **9.** Sidney is the more interesting.

_____ **10.** He is the most energetic of the family.

21 Practice

Complete the sentences using the superlative form of the words in parentheses.

1. For the marathon, we're looking for (fast) _____ runner, the person with (good) _____ time.

2. Tara won the contest for (original) _____ poem. It was (unusual) _____ one of all.

3. Our new house is nice, but we're going to change some things. We'll put plants in the living room because it's (bright) _____ room. The small bedroom is (dark) _____ one, and it has (old) _____ carpeting. Our bedroom is (big) _____, but it has (dark) _____ paint. The bathroom is (bad) _____ room in the house. This is (nice) _____ house I've ever lived in.

4. December 21st is (long) _____ night of the year in the northern hemisphere.

5. Cheryl is (popular) _____ girl at school.

6. Parachuting out of an airplane was (weird) _____, (exciting) _____, and (scary) _____ experience of my life!

7. The nurse speaks (gently) _____ with young patients.

8. My dog, Sherman, is (entertaining) _____ pet I've ever known!

22 Practice

Underline the correct form of the words in parentheses.

1. Eun Jun doesn't understand the assignment (as well as / the best) the rest of the class.

2. What's (the longest / longer than) river in the world?

3. Melissa is (the calmest / calmer than) I am in stressful situations.

4. Michael arrived (the latest / later than) of all.

5. Yoshimi's (the most reliable / more reliable than) student in the class.

6. That's (the most intelligent / more intelligent than) thing you've said.

7. It was (the most ridiculous/ more ridiculous than) last time.

8. Those families were (the most fortunate / more fortunate than) the ones who lost their homes.

9. Joan is (the nicest / nicer than) person I know.

10. Mr. Van Buren is (the least patient / less patient than) Ms. Cunningham.

11. Our new teacher speaks (the most quickly / more quickly than) of all.

12. Yesterday was (the worst / worse than) last Monday.

23 Practice

Answer the questions.

1. Which language do you speak the most fluently?

_____.

2. What's the easiest exercise in this book?

_____.

3. What's your earliest memory?

_____.

4. What's the most comfortable room in your home?

_____.

5. Who's the best student in your class?

_____.

6. What's your least favorite sport?

_____.

7. Who's the most creative person you know?

_____.

8. What's the most difficult challenge you've ever had in your life?

_____.

9. What's the worst movie in the world?

_____.

10. What's the most serious problem in your country?

_____.

10g Comparative and Superlative Forms of Nouns

Student Book 2 p. 284, Student Book 2B p. 92

24 Practice

Read the information about three companies for last year. Write sentences using *more ... than, fewer ... than, less ... than, the most ..., the fewest ..., the least ..., as many ... as, as much ... as.*

	Connect Net	SoftMagic	Webservice
Profits	$2,500,000	$2,250,000	$4,630,000
Number of employees	175	205	1,200
New accounts	22	37	93
Time/completed projects	3 months	5–6 months	4 months
Expected new hires for next year	10	0	10
Incomplete projects	5	3	15

1. *Connect Net made more money than SoftMagic* .

2. _____ .

3. _____ .

4. _____ .

5. _____ .

6. _____ .

7. _____ .

8. _____ .

9. _____ .

10. _____ .

11. _____ .

12. _____ .

Practice

Kevin, Tasha, and Tracy work for SoftMagic. Their managers have to lay off one of them. They are discussing each person's merits.

	Kevin	Tasha	Tracy
New customers/year	30	14	45
Work	90%	75%	100%
Overtime hours/week	15	3	20
Responsibilities in position	15	15	20
Salary	$60,000	$60,000	$71,000

1. _Kevin does more work than Tasha._ (OR)

   Tasha does less work than Kevin.

2. _____.

3. _____.

4. _____.

5. _____.

6. _____.

7. _____.

8. _____.

9. _____.

26 Practice

Read the statements and underline the correct form of the words in parentheses.

1. Ben and Sherry have (as many dogs as / as less dogs as) we do.

2. Which dish has (the fewest / the least) calories?

3. Last winter, we didn't have (as many bad weather as / as much bad weather as) we do this year.

4. Wow! That's (the more / the most) money I've ever seen!

5. She bought (much more clothes / many more clothes) this year than she did last year.

6. I get (many more news / much more news) from the morning paper.

7. Jesse's doing (the fewest / the least) work in the group.

8. Let's take the apartment with (the most / the fewest) space.

9. She got (much more / many more) votes than her opponent.

10. My dad doesn't have (as many hair as / as much hair as) he used to.

10h The Double Comparative

Student Book 2 p. 287, Student Book 2B p. 95

27 Practice

Rewrite the sentences using "comparative + *and* + comparative" and the underlined words.

1. It's becoming dark <u>early</u>.

   It's becoming dark earlier and earlier .

2. English is becoming <u>easy</u>.

   _____ .

3. Peggy's work is becoming <u>good</u>.

   _____ .

4. The children are becoming <u>responsible</u>.

   _____ .

Comparative and Superlative Forms

5. The neighborhood is becoming dangerous.

_____.

6. Living in this city is becoming expensive.

_____.

28 Practice

Write sentences using "_the_ + comparative clause, _the_ + comparative clause" and the underlined words.

1. Lisa <u>shouted</u>. Ted became <u>angry</u>.

   The more Lisa shouted, the angrier Ted became .

2. Ted got <u>angry</u>. The class became <u>nervous</u>.

   _____.

3. The class became <u>nervous</u>. They didn't pay <u>attention</u> to the assignment.

   _____.

4. I drove a <u>long</u> time. I got <u>tired</u>.

   _____.

5. I got <u>tired</u>. I <u>yawned</u> a lot.

   _____.

6. She <u>listened</u> to the lecture. She became <u>confused</u>.

   _____.

7. Stanley is <u>prepared</u>. His presentation will be <u>easy</u>.

   _____.

8. He <u>stayed</u> at work. He felt <u>sick</u>.

   _____.

9. I watch that movie <u>often</u>. I don't <u>like</u> it that much.

   _____.

10. Bill <u>works out</u>. He feels <u>good</u>.

   _____.

29 Practice

Read the double comparatives. Then write what they mean.

1. The more you know, the less you know.

2. The longer I study English, the easier it is to understand.

3. The more it snows, the happier I am.

4. The more you pay, the less you pay.

5. The longer I know her, the better I like her.

1. _When I learn something, I understand how much I don't know._

2. _____.

3. _____.

4. _____.

5. _____.

30 Practice

Complete the sentences about yourself.

1. The older I get, _____.

2. _____, the more I like it.

3. The more I exercise, _____.

4. _____, the more confused I get.

5. _____, the happier I am.

10i *The Same As, Similar To, Different From, Like,* and *Alike*

Student Book 2 p. 290, Student Book 2B p. 98

31 Practice

Write *C* next to the sentence if *the same as, similar to, different from, like,* or *alike* is used correctly. Write *I* if *the same as, similar to, different from, like,* or *alike* is used incorrectly.

_____ 1. Her car is similar to yours.

_____ 2. The climate here is different than the climate in South America.

_____ 3. My brother and I don't look alike at all.

_____ 4. Do teachers make as same money as nurses?

_____ **5.** Our jackets are similar to.

_____ **6.** His ideas are different from the department's.

_____ **7.** The paintings in this museum are alike to the ones we saw last year.

_____ **8.** Ellen and Irene have the same middle name.

_____ **9.** The names Eileen and Irene sound similar.

_____ **10.** All those houses look like.

32 Practice

Read the information about Art and his brother Andy. Then write sentences with _the same as, similar to, different from, like,_ or _alike_ and words from the list or your own.

Andy and Art are both 6 feet 3 inches tall. Art is 36, and Andy is 32. They have blue eyes and blond hair. Andy weighs 190 pounds, and Art weights 170 pounds. Andy is a programmer, and Art is a software engineer. They both live in San Jose, California. They both like fishing and hunting. Art went to college, but Andy didn't. Art drives a used economy car, but Andy drives a motorcycle.

| ages | education | hair | hobbies | vehicles |
| cities | eyes | height | jobs | weight |

1. _Art's education was different from Andy's._ (OR)

Their educations were different.

2. _____ .

3. _____ .

4. _____ .

5. _____ .

6. _____ .

7. _____ .

8. _____ .

9. _____ .

10. _____ .

A   Choose the best answer, A, B, C, or D, to complete the sentence. Mark your answer by darkening the oval with the same letter.

1. She got up _____.

   A. most sudden   Ⓐ Ⓑ Ⓒ Ⓓ
   B. suddenly
   C. sudden
   D. more sudden

2. Monster movies are _____.

   A. frightens   Ⓐ Ⓑ Ⓒ Ⓓ
   B. frightened
   C. most frightened
   D. frightening

3. Swimming is _____ running.

   A. strenuouser than   Ⓐ Ⓑ Ⓒ Ⓓ
   B. the more strenuous than
   C. more strenuous than
   D. the most strenuous than

4. Steve feels _____.

   A. weaked   Ⓐ Ⓑ Ⓒ Ⓓ
   B. weaking
   C. weak
   D. weakly

5. Dennis hasn't been as talkative _____ he used to be.

   A. as   Ⓐ Ⓑ Ⓒ Ⓓ
   B. than
   C. the same
   D. alike

6. Farmers have to get up _____ other people.

   A. the earliest   Ⓐ Ⓑ Ⓒ Ⓓ
   B. more early
   C. earlier than
   D. as early than

7. Brenda writes _____ of anyone in the office.

   A. less articulately than   Ⓐ Ⓑ Ⓒ Ⓓ
   B. as articulately as
   C. more articulately
   D. the most articulately

8. The research department needs _____ information.

   A. much more   Ⓐ Ⓑ Ⓒ Ⓓ
   B. many more
   C. fewer
   D. least

9. The more you give, _____.

   A. the most you get   Ⓐ Ⓑ Ⓒ Ⓓ
   B. the least you get
   C. more you get
   D. the more you get

10. That small company's software is similar _____ ours.

    A. than   Ⓐ Ⓑ Ⓒ Ⓓ
    B. to
    C. as
    D. alike

B **Find the underlined word or phrase, A, B, C, or D, that is incorrect. Mark your answer by darkening the oval with the same letter.**

1. The cake <u>smells</u> <u>good</u> and <u>tastes</u> <u>well</u>.
               A   B   C   D

   Ⓐ Ⓑ Ⓒ Ⓓ

2. <u>Finding</u> <u>good</u> bands is becoming
      A   B

   <u>the</u> <u>harder and harder</u>.
    C   D

   Ⓐ Ⓑ Ⓒ Ⓓ

3. We <u>didn't go</u> as <u>far</u> <u>than</u> <u>the other</u> team.
        A   B C   D

   Ⓐ Ⓑ Ⓒ Ⓓ

4. She was <u>the</u> <u>more</u> <u>beautiful</u> <u>woman</u> in
           A   B   C   D

   the room.

   Ⓐ Ⓑ Ⓒ Ⓓ

5. <u>Let's</u> take his car. It's <u>the</u> <u>bigger than</u>
    A   B   C

   <u>mine</u>.
    D

   Ⓐ Ⓑ Ⓒ Ⓓ

6. I feel <u>sickly</u>. I got up <u>more</u> <u>quickly</u>
        A   B   C

   <u>than</u> usual.
    D

   Ⓐ Ⓑ Ⓒ Ⓓ

7. Todd <u>sees</u> <u>better</u> <u>than</u> he did. These are
        A   B   C

   <u>the better</u> glasses he's ever had.
      D

   Ⓐ Ⓑ Ⓒ Ⓓ

8. <u>The bigger</u> <u>are they</u>, <u>the harder</u>
     A   B   C

   <u>they fall</u>.
    D

   Ⓐ Ⓑ Ⓒ Ⓓ

9. Joyce <u>has</u> <u>the</u> same CD <u>than</u> <u>I do</u>.
        A B   C   D

   Ⓐ Ⓑ Ⓒ Ⓓ

10. The pie <u>tastes</u> different <u>from</u> apples,
         A   B

    but <u>similar</u> <u>than</u> peaches.
       C   D

    Ⓐ Ⓑ Ⓒ Ⓓ

UNIT 11 THE PASSIVE VOICE

11a Active and Passive Voice Verbs: Simple Present, Simple Past, Present Perfect, Past Perfect, and Future Tenses

Student Book 2 p. 296, Student Book 2B p. 104

1 Practice

Read the sentences. Write *A* next to the sentence if it is in the active voice. Write *P* if it is in the passive voice.

_____ **1.** The owners of that house hired John and me to redo their backyard.

_____ **2.** We were very excited about doing the project.

_____ **3.** The garden was designed by us.

_____ **4.** We bought lots of flowers and plants at the nursery.

_____ **5.** It started raining.

_____ **6.** The flowers were chosen by me.

_____ **7.** It looks beautiful now.

_____ **8.** Hummingbirds love the new flowers.

_____ **9.** We weren't given a lot of time by the owners.

_____ **10.** Some of the roses have been picked by the children.

2 Practice

Clarissa is talking about her sister's last birthday party. Change the active sentences to passive sentences.

1. My grandmother made her this sweater.

 This sweater was made for her by my grandmother .

2. My grandmother gave it to my sister for her birthday.

_____ .

3. My mom baked a lemon cake.

_____ .

4. We played games.

_____ .

5. We sang songs.

_____.

6. We hit a piñata.

_____.

7. Her friends told jokes.

_____.

8. We ate ice cream.

_____.

9. She blew out the candles.

_____.

10. We had a great time!

_____.

3 **Practice**

Rewrite the following sentences. Change the active sentences to passive ones.

A. 1. My mechanic fixes my car.

   _My car is fixed by my mechanic_____.

2. He looked at it last week.

_____.

3. He'll change the oil tomorrow.

_____.

4. I'm going to pick it up tomorrow.

_____.

5. He should finish it by then.

_____.

6. Jordan and his brother have owned the garage for seven years.

_____.

B. 1. The workers are going to finish the house tomorrow.

_____.

2. They haven't painted it yet because someone stole the paint.

_____.

3. They've already installed the windows and carpeting.

_____.

4. *No one has bought it yet.

_____.

(* Make the verb negative and use _anyone._)

5. The agents are going to show it to the public next week.

_____.

6. We can see it then.

_____.

C. Daughter: Mom, can I go to the movies with Keith and Jenny?

Mom: Have you finished your chores?

_____?

Daughter: Yes. I've washed the dishes.

_____.

Daughter: And I've made my bed.

_____.

Daughter: I've finished my homework.

_____.

Daughter: I've already taken out the garbage.

_____.

Mom: Have you put your clean clothes away?

_____?

Daughter: Yes. I've done everything that you asked me to do.

_____.

D. Caleb: Are we ready for the meeting?

Merna: I think so. I've already made the coffee.

_____.

Caleb: I've put out the cookies.

_____.

Merna: Josh sets up the chairs, right?

_____?

Caleb: Yep. I'll hand out the papers.

_____.

Merna: Larry will collect the money.

_____.

Caleb: Stephanie will put away the chairs.

_____.

Merna: Jackie's going to wash the cups.

_____.

Caleb: Paulo will read the introduction.

_____.

Merna: I'll empty the trashcans.

_____.

Caleb: Thanks. Sarah will greet the new people.

_____.

E. Wife: What happened?!

Husband: Well, I didn't turn off the faucet.

_____.

I called a plumber _____,

but he didn't fix it. _____.

He needs a new part. _____.

F. Hideo: How do you play the game?

_____?

Shawna: I give each person some money, and then we roll the dice.

_____.

Then we move the pieces around the board.

_____.

I deal the cards.

_____.

When we reach the end, the game is over.

_____.

4 Practice

Complete the sentences with the active or the passive form of the verbs in parentheses.

A. 1. Millions of homes (destroy) _____ by fire last weekend.

2. Most people (escape) _____ without injury.

3. The fire (cause) _____ by lightning.

4. Sadly, some family pets (kill) _____ by the fire and smoke.

5. All the families (be) _____ happy to be safe.

6. Some personal items (find) _____ by the fire fighters.

7. Luckily, the wind (change) _____ directions.

8. A few families (think) _____ about rebuilding.

9. The fire (put out) _____ by the fire fighters.

B. 1. The restaurant (be) _____ open from 9:00 A.M. – 10:00 P.M.

2. Breakfast (serve) _____ all day.

3. Three dinner specials (offer) _____ every day.

4. They (know) _____ for their seafood.

5. There (be) _____ no smoking in the restaurant.

6. Bread (make) _____ fresh daily.

7. Reservations (recommend) _____.

8. They (offer) _____ a Sunday brunch.

9. Finding the restaurant (be) _____ easy.

10. Parking (be) _____ available.

5 Practice

Answer the questions.

1. Who is your favorite book written by?

   _____

2. Who is your favorite song sung by?

   _____

3. Who was this book printed by?

   _____

4. Who was your city founded by?

   _____

5. How many people is your language spoken by?

   _____

11b The *By* Phrase

Student Book 2 p. 303, Student Book 2B p. 111

6 Practice

Read the sentences. Write *N* next to the sentence if the agent (with a *by* phrase) is needed because it is important to the writer's meaning. Write *U* if the agent is unnecessary.

_____ 1. These cars were made by people in Japan.

_____ 2. The lightbulb was invented by Thomas Edison.

_____ 3. Those houses were built by people in the 1900s.

_____ 4. The bridge was built by engineers in 1953.

_____ 5. The dress was designed by a famous French designer.

_____ 6. *Harry Potter* was written by J.K. Rowling.

_____ 7. The ballet *The Nutcracker* was written by Tchaikovsky.

_____ 8. Her wallet was stolen by someone.

_____ 9. Fresh flowers are delivered by the florist every day.

_____ 10. I was taught English by English teachers for three years in high school.

7 Practice

Change the passive sentences to active ones. Use a logical agent for the *by* **clause if there isn't one.**

1. Those fish were caught in the Pacific Ocean this morning.

   People caught those fish in the Pacific Ocean this morning .

2. Mistakes were made.

   _____ .

3. The apartment building was built in the 1960s.

   _____ .

4. Our class photograph is going to be taken tomorrow.

   _____ .

5. The telephone was invented by Alexander Graham Bell.

   _____ .

6. My room was painted by my parents.

   _____ .

7. Chocolate is made from cacao beans.

   _____ .

8. The TV had already been turned on.

   _____ .

9. Many electronics are imported from Asia.

   _____ .

10. Martin Luther King, Jr. was awarded the Nobel Peace Prize in 1964.

    _____ .

11. The garbage will be picked up tomorrow morning.

_____.

12. The Statue of Liberty was given to the United States by France.

_____.

8 | Practice

Read the sentences about zoos. Change the sentences to the passive voice. Use the _by_ phrase only when necessary. Use the correct verb tense.

1. Queen Hatshepsut of ancient Egypt built the first zoo in 1500 B.C.

_____.

2. People gave animals to pharaohs as gifts.

_____.

3. The Chinese emperor Wen Wang created the Garden of Intelligence around 1000 B.C.

_____.

4. The Greeks built the first public zoos to study plants and animals.

_____.

5. People created many small zoos in North Africa, China, and India between 1000 B.C. and 400 B.C.

_____.

6. In the 13th century, King Henry III brought the first elephant to England.

_____.

7. Someone gave it to him as a present.

_____.

8. People consider the Vienna Zoo the oldest zoo in the world.

_____.

9. People opened it in 1752.

_____.

Practice

Read the sentences. Change the active sentences to passive ones. Use the *by* phrase only when necessary. Use the correct verb tense.

1. Andy and Larry Wachowski wrote and directed the movie *The Matrix*.

   _____.

2. Thousands of people saw it.

   _____.

3. People made the movie in 1999.

   _____.

4. It made $22.2 million the first week it opened.

   _____.

5. In the movie, computers control the human environment.

   _____.

6. One of the characters, Morpheus, discovers the hero, Neo.

   _____.

7. Neo saves the world.

   _____.

10 Practice

Answer the questions.

1. What languages are spoken in your country?

   _____.

2. What subjects are taught at your school?

   _____.

3. What sports are shown on TV in the spring?

   _____.

4. What holidays are celebrated in the winter?

   _____.

5. What is your country known for?

   _____.

11c The Passive Form of the Present Progressive and Past Progressive Tenses

Student Book 2 p. 306, Student Book 2B p. 114

11 Practice

A manager of a busy pizza restaurant is talking about what's happening in the restaurant. Complete the sentences using the present progressive passive form of the verbs in parentheses.

1. Orders (take) _are being taken_____.

2. Pizzas (make) _____.

3. Reservations (take) _____.

4. Tables (clean off) _____.

5. Dishes (wash) _____.

6. People (seat) _____.

7. Customers (serve) _____.

8. Bills (pay) _____.

9. Tips (leave) _____.

10. At the tables, jokes (tell) _____.

Who is doing the tasks listed above? Match the tasks with the job title.

busser   cashier   cook   customers   dishwasher   host   server

1. __server__   6. _____

2. _____   7. _____

3. _____   8. _____

4. _____   9. _____

5. _____   10. _____

12 Practice

There is a terrible accident near Sydney's house. Read what is happening. Complete the sentences with the present progressive passive of the verbs in parentheses.

One car (tow) _____, and the other car (photograph) _____.

1
2

Some people (take away) _____ in the ambulance, and some other people

3

(interview) _____ by the police.
4

One driver (give) _____ a ticket.
5

13 Practice

Lynn flew home to help with her brother's wedding last fall. Read the sentences and complete them with the past progressive active or past progressive passive form of the verbs in parentheses.

1. My brother (get) _____ married, and he (plan)

   _____ a big wedding.

2. When I got there, a lot of things (happen) _____.

3. Guest (fly) _____ in.

4. The tent (rent) _____.

5. His tuxedo (fit) _____.

6. Food (cater) _____.

7. A lot of money (spend) _____.

8. I (get) _____ tired from watching everything!

14 Practice

Change the passive sentences to active ones. Use a logical agent for the *by* clause if there isn't one.

1. The rooms are being painted pink!

   _The painters are painting the rooms pink_____!

2. The supermodels were being interviewed by a magazine writer at 4:00.

   _____.

3. The computer was being repaired when I called the shop.

   _____.

4. We're being tested on Monday.

   _____.

5. The new furniture was being assembled when they left.

_____.

6. Your clothes are being washed right now.

_____.

11d The Passive Forms of Modals

Student Book 2 p. 309, Student Book 2B p. 117

15 Practice

Complete the sentences using the passive form of the modal and verb in parentheses.

1. Red wine (should / serve) ___should be served___ at room temperature.

2. Milk (must / put) _____ in the refrigerator.

3. Pizza (can / eat) _____ cold.

4. Anything that touches raw meat (have to / wash) _____ well.

5. Ice (must / make) _____ in the freezer.

6. Popcorn (can / pop) _____ in the microwave.

7. Tomatoes (should / not / keep) _____ in the refrigerator.

8. Juice (have to / put) _____ in the refrigerator after you open it.

9. Tofu (can / keep) _____ fresh in the refrigerator.

10. Dinner (ought to / eat) _____ in the dining room.

16 Practice

Tom has just bought a car, and he is reading some of the rules online. Change the active sentences to passive ones. Use the _by_ phrase only when necessary.

1. You can register your car on the Internet.

_____.

2. You must insure your car.

_____.

3. You must keep your driver's license with you at all times.

_____.

4. You must pay the fees by the due date.

_____.

5. If payment isn't received, the Department of Motor Vehicles will cancel your registration.

_____.

6. If you park your car on the street, a police officer might ticket it.

_____.

7. The Department of Motor Vehicles will not refund your money after you send it.

_____.

8. If you have more questions, you can contact the Department of Motor Vehicles for information.

_____.

17 Practice

Read the sentences. Write *A* next to the sentence if it is in the active voice. Write *P* if it is in the passive voice.

_____ **1.** We should call Harriet. She wasn't feeling well yesterday.

_____ **2.** The coffee can be made in the morning.

_____ **3.** Your clothes should be hung up.

_____ **4.** The letters must be sent out tomorrow.

_____ **5.** Doyle's having a good time.

_____ **6.** Jeanne couldn't have pets when she was growing up.

_____ **7.** Richard and the kids will meet us at the park.

_____ **8.** The game has to be finished quickly.

_____ **9.** Cindy had to leave. There was an emergency.

_____ **10.** You should go to the basement in a tornado.

Practice

Answer the questions with your own ideas.

1. What can be done about world hunger?

   _____.

2. What should be done about pollution?

   _____.

3. What ought to pass from parents to their children?

   _____.

4. What energy sources will be used in the future?

   _____.

5. What new medicines might be discovered 50 years from now?

   _____.

11e *Have* Something *Done*

Student Book 2 p. 311, Student Book 2B p. 119

19 Practice

The Andersons have just bought their first house. What will they have done before they move in?

build a garage   insulate the attic
check the electricity   paint the rooms
clean out the basement   put in a garden
cut the grass   put in new windows   repair the leaks
fix the roof   remove the carpeting replace the old stove

1. *They're going to have a garage built*_____.

2. _____.

3. _____.

4. _____.

5. _____.

6. _____.

7. _____.

8. _____ .

9. _____ .

10. _____ .

11. _____ .

12. _____ .

20 Practice

What do the sentences mean? Write them in another way.

1. Jessica had her sister pick up her children.

   Jessica asked her sister to pick up her children .

2. Peggy has her nails done every week.

   Peggy pays someone to take care of her fingernails .

3. We're going to have the bookcases assembled.

   _____ .

4. We had our reunion photos taken by a professional photographer.

   _____ .

5. Have they had the photos developed yet?

   _____ ?

6. Donna had her car washed.

   _____ .

7. Cheryl is having her phone number changed.

   _____ .

21 Practice

You have a housekeeper, a cook, a chauffeur, and an assistant. What will you have done for you today?

1. _I'll have my clothes ironed_ .

2. _____ .

3. _____ .

4. _____ .

5. _____ .

Your best friend has lost a bet with you. Now he/she will do whatever you ask him/her to do for one day. What are you going to have him/her do for you?

6. _I'm going to have him/her do my homework_ .

7. _____ .

8. _____ .

9. _____ .

10. _____ .

11f More Transitive Phrasal Verbs with Objects: Separable

Student Book 2 p. 313, Student Book 2B p. 121

22 Practice

Write C next to the sentence if the pronoun is in the correct place. Write I if the pronoun is not in the correct place.

_____ **1.** Can you turn up it?

_____ **2.** Turn it down! I can't hear anything.

_____ **3.** Dean is calling it off.

_____ **4.** Put them back in their boxes.

_____ **5.** When you're finished, shut it off.

_____ **6.** Maria is trying them on now.

_____ **7.** Krystal's going to take back them in the morning.

_____ **8.** When are you going to pay back me?

_____ **9.** Why don't you call up her?

23 Practice

Read the situations. Complete the sentences with the correct separable phrasal verb.

a. shut off

b. hasn't paid me back

c. 're calling off

d. turns up

e. put it back

f. try them on

g. took them back

h. turns it down

i. call up

A. Joshua: They _____ the conference.

Nella: Why?

Joshua: Not very many people can come.

Nella: Is someone going to _____ everyone and tell them?

Joshua: Yes, Aaron is.

B. Sue: First Bill borrowed money to buy some shoes he liked, but after two days

he decided he didn't like them, so he _____.

Barry: Did he _____ before he bought them?

Sue: I don't know. All I know is that he _____ yet.

C. Helen and Adrienne are sisters and they share a room. Helen likes to study with

music on, so she _____ the radio. However, Adrienne needs a quiet place

when she does her homework, so she _____ when she's in the room.

D. Please _____ the computer before you leave. Don't waste electricity.

E. Tyler! We're not buying ice cream today. Take it out of the cart and _____

right now.

24 | Practice

Underline the correct phrasal verb in parentheses.

1. Adam has just (called me up / paid me back). Let's get some coffee. I'll buy!

2. This sweater has a hole in it. You should (take it back / try it on).

3. You need to (call off the engine / shut off the engine) when you're in the garage.

4. Someone borrowed Vince's tape recorder, and they haven't (put it back / turned it down).

5. Let's (call Nicole up / take Nicole back) and ask her to come with us.

6. Wow! Can you (take back / turn down) the TV? It's too loud.

7. I hate (trying on / paying back) clothes in department stores. The mirrors and lights make me look terrible.

8. I love this song! (Turn it up / Turn it down), please.

A **Choose the best answer, A, B, C, or D, to complete the sentence. Mark your answer by darkening the oval with the same letter.**

1. This bread _____ in a bakery.

   A. was making   Ⓐ Ⓑ Ⓒ Ⓓ
   B. is making
   C. made
   D. was made

2. Don't worry. The children _____.

   A. are taking care of   Ⓐ Ⓑ Ⓒ Ⓓ
   B. are being taken care of
   C. is being taken care of
   D. was taken care of

3. Herman is trying _____ the boots.

   A. back   Ⓐ Ⓑ Ⓒ Ⓓ
   B. off
   C. on
   D. up

4. The biology department is making the test.

   A. The test is being made by the biology
      department.   Ⓐ Ⓑ Ⓒ Ⓓ
   B. The test was being made by the
      biology department.
   C. The test is made by the biology
      department.
   D. The test is making by the biology
      department.

5. Joe hasn't _____ me back.

   A. called   Ⓐ Ⓑ Ⓒ Ⓓ
   B. turned
   C. put
   D. shut

6. Harrison is _____ his laundry done.

   A. have   Ⓐ Ⓑ Ⓒ Ⓓ
   B. had
   C. having
   D. has

7. Cabbage _____ on this farm.

   A. grown   Ⓐ Ⓑ Ⓒ Ⓓ
   B. are grown
   C. growing
   D. is grown

8. That old milk _____.

   A. should throw out   Ⓐ Ⓑ Ⓒ Ⓓ
   B. should be thrown out
   C. should be throw out
   D. throw out

9. Help! We _____.

   A. attack by bees   Ⓐ Ⓑ Ⓒ Ⓓ
   B. are attacked by bees
   C. are attacking by bees
   D. are being attacked by bees

10. Our meeting _____.

    A. called off   Ⓐ Ⓑ Ⓒ Ⓓ
    B. was called off
    C. is calling off
    D. calls off

B **Find the underlined word or phrase, A, B, C, or D, that is incorrect. Mark your answer by darkening the oval with the same letter.**

1. The party <u>was hold</u> at the garden club.
   A

   It <u>didn't rain</u>, so it <u>wasn't</u> <u>called off</u>.
   B   C   D

   Ⓐ Ⓑ Ⓒ Ⓓ

2. Most of the <u>cars</u> <u>parked</u> in the garage,
   A B

   but Donny's <u>having</u> his car <u>washed</u>.
   C   D

   Ⓐ Ⓑ Ⓒ Ⓓ

3. She was <u>having</u> her hair <u>cut</u> when I
   A   B

   <u>called</u> up <u>her</u>.
   C   D

   Ⓐ Ⓑ Ⓒ Ⓓ

4. The race <u>was</u> <u>won</u> <u>by someone</u> in
   A B C

   90 <u>minutes</u>.
   D

   Ⓐ Ⓑ Ⓒ Ⓓ

5. Mr. Swanson <u>thought</u> his car <u>stolen</u>, but
   A   B

   his son had borrowed it and hadn't

   <u>put</u> <u>it</u> back in the garage.
   C D

   Ⓐ Ⓑ Ⓒ Ⓓ

6. *Romeo and Juliet* <u>was written</u>
   A

   <u>Shakespeare</u>. It's <u>been</u> <u>translated</u> into
   B   C D

   many languages.

   Ⓐ Ⓑ Ⓒ Ⓓ

7. I just <u>turned</u> down <u>it</u>. Who <u>turned it</u> <u>up</u>?
   A   B   C   D

   Ⓐ Ⓑ Ⓒ Ⓓ

8. Are you going to <u>try</u> the coat? If it
   A

   doesn't fit, you can't <u>take</u> <u>it</u> <u>back</u>.
   B C D

   Ⓐ Ⓑ Ⓒ Ⓓ

9. Alfonso's son <u>is</u> <u>fascinated</u> <u>by dinosaurs</u>.
   A B   C

   He's also <u>interest</u> in ancient Egypt.
   D

   Ⓐ Ⓑ Ⓒ Ⓓ

10. The document <u>signed</u>
    A

    <u>by the country's leaders</u>. Finally an
    B

    agreement <u>had been</u> <u>reached</u>.
    C   D

    Ⓐ Ⓑ Ⓒ Ⓓ

UNIT 12 CONJUNCTIONS AND NOUN CLAUSES

12a The Conjunctions *And*, *But*, and *Or*

Student Book 2 p. 320, Student Book 2B p. 128

1 | **Practice**

Read the conversations. Complete the sentences with *and* or *or*.

1. **A:** Would you like milk _____ sugar?

   B: Yes, please.

2. **A:** Would you like milk _____ sugar?

   B: Sugar, please.

3. **A:** Does she want to see a comedy _____ an action film?

   B: No, she only has time to see one.

4. **A:** Does she want to see a comedy _____ an action film?

   B: A comedy.

5. **A:** Did you order rice _____ pasta?

   B: I got the rice.

6. **A:** Did you order rice _____ pasta?

   B: Yes, I'm starving!

7. **A:** Shall we stay here _____ go out later?

   B: That sounds good.

8. **A:** Shall we stay here _____ go out later?

   B: Let's stay here.

9. **A:** Does your sister write with her left _____ her right hand?

   B: Yes, both.

10. **A:** Does your sister write with her left _____ her right hand?

    B: She's left-handed.

2 Practice

Read the information about the Coliseum.
Complete the sentences with *and* or *but*.

The Coliseum was built in A.D. 72. It had 80

entrances _____ could hold 50,000
                    1

people. The people in the upper class had marble

seats, _____ the lower classes sat on benches. There were many events in the
              2

Coliseum. There were gladiator fights, naval battles, _____ wild animal hunts,
                                                                3

_____ later, the naval battles were moved to a different location. After
         4

A.D. 404, gladiators didn't fight there, _____ wild animals fought there instead.
                                                  5

Today, the Coliseum is one of the most visited places in Rome, _____ is a
                                                                            6

fine example of ancient Roman architecture.

3 Practice

Complete the sentences with *and, or,* or *but*.

1. It was supposed to be finished tomorrow, _____ it's not going to be.

2. Mei's alarm woke her up at 6:00 this morning, _____ she turned it off

_____ went back to sleep.

3. Mark graduated with a degree in advertising _____ started working at a

large company.

4. We have a choice. We can work full time for less money _____ part time for

more money per hour.

5. In Europe, do people mostly drive to work _____ take public transportation?

6. Ryan's starving. He's having soup _____ salad.

7. Sarah and Steven watched the sun set _____ the stars appear.

8. Do you work better in the morning _____ at night?

9. I heard a knock on the door, _____ there was no one there.

4 Practice

Change the conjunction to correct the sentence.

1. Trina usually doesn't like scary movies, <u>or</u> she liked this one.

   _____.

2. In my program, we can choose to write a paper <u>but</u> take a test. I chose the test.

   _____.

3. My kids love ice cream. Tony likes vanilla <u>or</u> chocolate, too.

   _____.

4. Do I turn right <u>and</u> left?

   _____.

5. Greg's finished his English homework, <u>or</u> he hasn't done the biology report yet.

   _____.

6. Erika has to take one more class. She might take "History of Film" <u>and</u> "Music Appreciation."

   _____.

7. The Stevensons have enough time, <u>or</u> they don't have enough money to travel.

   _____.

5 Practice

Add commas where necessary. Some sentences do not need commas.

1. Teddy has a cell phone books notebooks pens and his lunch in his backpack.

2. Toru put the car in the garage but forgot to lock it.

3. Hannah wants to see a movie and then get something to eat.

4. John needs something to read but the library is closed.

5. Claire can come up or we can go down there.

6. I'd like to meet you there but I'm not sure how to get there.

7. The team might come back here or stay overnight in the city.

8. Do you prefer Italian or Chinese food?

9. Hans tried to take the bus but the driver didn't understand what he was saying.

10. Kim's going to work late and her friend will pick her up later.

12b The Conjunction *So*

Student Book 2 p. 323, Student Book 2B p. 131

6 **Practice**

Read the sentences. Combine them using *so*.

1. He went shopping. Jeff had a little time.

    _Jeff had a little time, so he went shopping_____.

2. Leo is becoming more and more interested in business. He's thinking about

    changing his major.

    _____.

3. We haven't finished the project yet. She hasn't given us all the information.

    _____.

4. Gene had to help a classmate. He won't be joining the group later.

    _____.

5. Bert forgot to put money in the meter. He got a parking ticket.

    _____.

6. She's going to take Russian next year. Lauren is good at languages.

    _____.

7. It's a holiday. Mail isn't being delivered.

    _____.

8. When his boss asked him about the situation, he got scared. He lied about it.

    _____.

9. My stepson is very depressed. He's not going to classes.

    _____.

10. They've decided to break up. Gabe and Angela have been unhappy for a while.

    _____.

Practice
Change the conjunction to correct the sentence. Use *and, or, but,* or *so.*

1. She didn't feel well, <u>or</u> she went home.

   She didn't feel well, so she went home.

2. Andy told us he'll be there, <u>so</u> I think he's too busy to come.

   _____.

3. Do you want to take the elevator <u>but</u> the stairs?

   _____.

4. Heather couldn't find the information in English, <u>and</u> she looked for it in her native language, German.

   _____.

5. The sky is clear, <u>or</u> the sun is shining.

   _____.

6. Ricardo's allergic to milk, <u>but</u> he doesn't eat ice cream.

   _____.

7. Carter paid a lot of money to have his room painted, <u>so</u> he doesn't like it.

   _____.

8. Call me <u>but</u> email me when you decide what you're going to do.

   _____.

9. Jack needed some cereal and fruit, <u>and</u> he stopped at the grocery store.

   _____.

10. Danielle has to deposit her paycheck, <u>so</u> she has to pick up her dry cleaning.

    _____.

Read the story called "Stone Soup."

A long time ago, a man walked into a village. He
didn't have any food. He was very hungry. He asked
some of the villagers for something to eat, but they
didn't want to give their food to him. He had an idea.
He told the people in the village he was going to make
stone soup. The man put a pot of water on a fire and put a stone in it. Soon everyone
came to watch him. "Mmm," the man said. "This is going to be delicious. Too bad I don't
have any cabbage. Stone soup with cabbage is really something!" One of the villagers went
to her house and brought back some cabbage to put in the pot. "Now, this is really special
stone soup. The only thing better than this is stone soup and cabbage with a little beef in
it!" An old man quickly went to his house and returned with a small piece of beef. The
man said, "Amazing! You will never taste anything like this again. Now if only we had a
small onion..." A young girl ran to her house. When she came back, she had two small
onions with her. The man cut them up and added them to the soup. Soon everyone
brought a little of what they had in their homes. Everyone had a bowl of delicious stone
soup. The villagers learned something. When everyone shares what he or she has, everyone
has enough.

Now complete the sentences about the story using *so*.

1. He didn't have any food, so _____.

2. The villagers didn't give him any food, so _____

_____.

3. He told the people that stone soup is really good with cabbage, so _____

_____.

4. Then he told them that stone soup is really good with beef, so_____

_____.

5. A young girl brought back two onions, so _____.

6. Everyone brought something from home, so _____.

7. Everyone added to the soup, so _____.

9 Practice

Complete the sentences with *so* and your own ideas.

1. I didn't sleep well, _____.

2. I didn't finish the homework, _____.

3. I dislike cold weather, _____.

4. There are six billion people in the world, _____.

5. I locked my keys in my car, _____.

6. I forgot your phone number, _____.

7. I didn't understand what the teacher said, _____.

8. I don't work out a lot, _____.

9. I _____,

     so _____.

10. I _____,

     so _____.

12c *Too, So, Either,* and *Neither*

Student Book 2 p. 325, Student Book 2B p. 133

10 Practice

Write *C* next to the dialogue if *too, so, either,* or *neither* is used correctly. Write *I* if *too, so, either,* or *neither* is used incorrectly.

   I   **1. A:** We didn't have enough money to pay the fees.

             B: So did she.

  _____   **2. A:** Fenny can't speak French well yet.

             B: Her brother can't yet, either.

  _____   **3. A:** Mickey was here.

             B: Neither was Allen.

_____ 4. **A:** I won't do that again.

  B: So will we!

_____ 5. **A:** Jim's worried about the situation.

  B: Neither are we.

_____ 6. **A:** She doesn't eat red meat.

  B: I don't either.

_____ 7. **A:** We love playing cards.

  B: My parents do, too.

_____ 8. **A:** Deborah's looking up some words in her dictionary.

  B: Neither does Thomas.

_____ 9. **A:** Julie can't set up her DVD player.

  B: My cousin can, too.

_____ 10. **A:** Several students didn't understand the lecture.

  B: Neither did I.

Rewrite the incorrect sentences to correct the agreement. If no change is necessary, write "no change."

1. **A:** We didn't have enough money to pay the fees.

  B: _Neither did she._ (OR) _She didn't, either._

2. _____.

3. _____.

4. _____.

5. _____.

6. _____.

7. _____.

8. _____.

9. _____.

10. _____.

11 Practice

Read the statements. Match the appropriate response to the statement.

_____ **1.** Anna's from Toronto.

_____ **2.** Ross doesn't like noisy restaurants.

_____ **3.** Max can't draw.

_____ **4.** We've finished dinner.

_____ **5.** Sam will work well with Mike.

_____ **6.** Terry apologized.

a. We will, too.

b. So have they.

c. So did Kim.

d. Neither do I.

e. Tony can't either.

f. I am, too!

12 Practice

Read the statements. Complete the agreements in two ways using _too, so, either,_ or _neither_.

Yoon and Sam have worked all weekend on a big project.

1. Yoon: I haven't quite finished my part of the

project.

Sam: Neither _____.

(OR) _____, either.

2. Yoon: But I'm exhausted!

Sam: So _____. (OR)

_____, too.

3. Yoon: I don't want to work too late this evening.

Sam: Neither _____. (OR)

_____, either.

4. Yoon: I'm going home now.

Sam: So _____. (OR)

_____, too.

5. Yoon: I'll be here early tomorrow morning.

Sam: So _____. (OR)

_____, too.

13 Practice

Read the statements. Complete the agreements in two ways using *too, so, either,* or *neither*.

Karen and Paul have had a big argument.

1. Karen: I'm still angry.

   Paul: So _____. (OR)

   _____, too.

2. Karen: You haven't apologized.

   Paul: Neither _____. (OR)

   _____, either.

3. Karen: I don't want to talk about it anymore.

   Paul: Neither _____. (OR)

   _____, either.

4. Karen: My feelings are hurt.

   Paul: So _____. (OR)

   _____, too.

5. Karen: I need some time alone.

   Paul: So _____. (OR)

   _____, too.

14 Practice

Complete the sentences with your own ideas. Pay attention to the verb tenses and auxiliaries.

1. _I love to shop in thrift stores_, and so does my mom.

2. _____, and neither do I.

3. _____, and my best friend doesn't, either.

4. _____, and so can my friends.

5. _____, and I will, too.

6. _____, and neither are my parents.

7. _____, and I didn't, either.

8. _____, and so am I.

Practice

Read the statements. Agree or disagree, and write sentences about yourself with *too, so, either,* or *neither.*

1. I love rainy days.

   _____*I don't.*_____ (OR) _*I do, too!*_ (OR) _*So do I.*_

2. I'm sleepy right now.

   _____.

3. I can't sing well.

   _____.

4. I like to cook.

   _____.

5. I can't drive a motorcycle.

   _____.

6. I'm good at drawing.

   _____.

7. I'm not good at tennis.

   _____.

8. I like Formula One.

   _____.

9. I'm not really interested in politics.

   _____.

10. I love animals!

    _____.

12d Noun Clauses Beginning with Wh- Words

Student Book 2 p. 329, Student Book 2B p. 137

16 Practice

Write *C* next to the sentence if the wh- noun clause is correct. Write *I* if the wh- noun clause is incorrect.

_____ 1. The instructor wasn't sure what the student was saying.

_____ 2. My daughter doesn't remember what is she supposed to do.

_____ 3. Brendan doesn't know why he wasn't chosen.

_____ 4. Michelle and Stan are wondering when they can pick up their new car.

_____ 5. We didn't know what were they doing.

_____ 6. Do you know who wrote that book?

_____ 7. Do they know where they're going on vacation?

_____ 8. Most people believe what they see.

_____ 9. Yuhei was wondering where could he park.

_____ 10. Everyone's wondering when is the new guy starting.

17 Practice

Read the conversations. Correct the questions by changing the underlined question forms to noun clauses.

1. Jason: Can you tell me <u>where is Second Street</u>?

    where Second Street is?

    Sally: It's near Pinecrest Street.

    Jason: I don't know <u>where is that</u>.

    _____

    Sally: Go straight two blocks and you will see it.

2. Zach: Do you know <u>what time is it</u>?

    _____

    Courtney: Yes, it's 2:15.

    Zach: Thanks. I am really late. I don't know <u>where did the time go</u>.

    _____

3. Lilly: Do you know <u>how do I change my password</u>?

_____

Seth: Sorry. I don't.

4. June: I wonder <u>how is he doing</u>.

_____

Pierre: Do you know <u>when can we visit him</u>?

_____

5. A: Do you know <u>why is he angry</u>?

_____

B: Something happened, but I'm not sure <u>what was it</u>.

_____

18 Practice

**It's Lucas's first day working in a large department store.
No one has trained him yet. Read the conversation.
Complete the sentences with noun clauses.**

1. Customer #1: Excuse me, where is the shoe department?

Lucas: Oh, I'm not sure

_____.

2. Customer #1: Well, I also need the restrooms. Where are they?

Lucas: I don't know _____.

3. Customer #2: When do you open on Saturdays?

Lucas: I'm sorry. I don't know _____.

4. Customer #2: How much is this?

Lucas: I'm not sure _____.

5. Customer #3: What's the price on this? I can't read it.

Lucas: I'm not certain _____.

6. Customer #3: What size is this? It's not marked.

Lucas: I really don't know _____.

19 Practice

It's Jenny's first day at a new high school. Read the conversation.
Underline the noun clauses.

Martin: Hi. What's your name?

Jenny: My name's Jenny. What's yours?

Martin: I'm Martin. Where are you going?

Jenny: I'm not sure where I'm going because I don't know where my next class is.

Martin: What class is it?

Jenny: It's geography.

Martin: I'm in that class. You can come with me.

Jenny: Do you know how difficult it is?

Martin: It's not bad. You'll be fine.

20 Practice

Write common questions for your classmates about the following topics.
Use *could you tell me* and the words in parentheses.

1. time (what/be)

   Could you tell me what time it is _____?

2. homework (what/be)

   _____?

3. new words (what/mean)

   _____?

4. the next test (when/be)

   _____?

5. lunch (when/be)

   _____?

12e Noun Clauses Beginning with *If* or *Whether*

Student Book 2 p. 333, Student Book 2B p. 141

21 Practice

Dan wants to ask Mimi out on a date to a movie and a Chinese restaurant. He's very nervous. Read the questions he's asking himself. Change the questions to noun clauses.

1. Will she say 'yes'?

   He doesn't know _if she will say yes (or not)_____.

2. Does she like romantic movies?

   He's wondering _____.

3. Does she like Chinese food?

   He's not certain _____.

4. Should I get a haircut?

   He doesn't know _____.

5. Should we have dinner first and then go to the movie?

   He's wondering _____.

6. Is my good jacket clean?

   He's not sure _____.

7. Do I have enough gas in the car?

   He's wondering _____.

8. Should I get more money out of the bank?

   He's not sure _____.

9. Will we have a good time?

   He doesn't know _____.

22 Practice

Nancy is making a cake. Her friend Alfonso doesn't think Nancy has followed the directions correctly. Read the questions he's asking himself. Change the questions to noun clauses.

1. Did she turn on the oven?

   Alfonso isn't sure <u>*whether or not Nancy turned on the oven*</u>.

2. Did she add enough sugar?

   He isn't certain _____.

3. Did she butter the pan?

   He is wondering _____.

4. Did she mix it well?

   He's asking himself _____.

5. Will she let the cake cool before she cuts it?

   He doesn't know _____.

6. Is the cake done now?

   He is wondering _____.

23 Practice

Read the sentences. Write *C* next to the sentence if *if (or not)* or *whether (or not)* is used correctly. Write *I* if *if (or not)* or *whether (or not)* is used incorrectly.

_____ 1. She's wondering whether or not she left the lights on.

_____ 2. I don't know if or not I'll have time to go with you.

_____ 3. The class wasn't sure whether the test was on Thursday or Friday.

_____ 4. My wife can't remember whether our reservations are at 6:00 or not.

_____ 5. Do you know if or not we're taking the train?

_____ 6. I wonder if we should bring something to eat or not.

_____ 7. I don't know whether my computer works with my printer or not.

_____ 8. June isn't sure if or not she should study business.

_____ 9. Do you remember if we're supposed to lock the door?

_____ 10. I wonder whether or not it'll rain tonight.

24 Practice

Kelly listens to the radio for the answers to the following questions. Complete the sentences with noun clauses.

1. Is the traffic bad downtown today?
2. What's the weather like?
3. Is it going to rain?
4. Is there any new news today?
5. What's the soccer score?
6. When's the next election?

1. Kelly wants to know *if the traffic is bad downtown today* .

2. Kelly wants to know _____.

3. Kelly wants to know _____.

4. Kelly wants to know _____.

5. Kelly wants to know _____.

6. Kelly wants to know _____.

25 Practice

Nathan is telling his friend Tiffany about a new restaurant. Use questions from the list to make noun clauses to complete the conversation.

Do I need to make reservations?	Can you smoke?
Do they accept checks?	Is there parking?
Are they open for breakfast?	Is the food good?

Tiffany: *Do you know if there's parking* ?
 ¹

Nathan: Yes, you can park in the back.

Tiffany: _____

 _____ ?
 ²

Nathan: No, no smoking.

Tiffany: _____

 _____ ?
 ³

Nathan: No, they don't. Just cash or credit cards.

Tiffany:	_____ ?
	4
Nathan:	Yes, they are.
Tiffany:	_____ ?
	5
Nathan:	No, they aren't necessary. It's not usually crowded.
Tiffany:	_____ ?
	6
Nathan:	It's delicious!

12f Noun Clauses Beginning with *That*

Student Book 2 p. 336, Student Book 2B p. 144

26 Practice

Two hikers are lost in the mountains. Read the interview from the news. Replace the underlined sections with *so* or *not*.

TV Announcer:	Stacey and Ken Brown were reported missing early this morning. Searchers are looking for them now. They don't know if they are safe, but they believe <u>they are</u>. Now our reporter Eugene Cisneros is interviewing Clinton Marx, the head searcher.
	1
Reporter:	Clinton, do you think they were heading east on the trail?
Head searcher:	We're not sure, but we believe <u>they were</u>.
	2
Reporter:	Do you have anything new to report?
Head searcher:	I'm afraid <u>I don't</u>.
	3
Reporter:	What's the weather going to be like tonight?
Head searcher:	It might snow tonight, but we hope <u>it won't</u>.
	4
Reporter:	Will you have anything new to report tomorrow?
Head searcher:	Yes, we think <u>we will</u>.
	5

1. _____

2. _____

3. _____

4. _____

5. _____

Practice

Read the questions. Agree or disagree using *so* or *not* and *think, believe, be afraid,* or *guess*. Explain why or why not.

1. Should professional athletes make a lot of money?

   I don't believe so. I think teachers should make a lot of money.

2. Should governments spend money on space exploration?

   _____.

3. Should people download music from the Internet and not pay for it?

   _____.

4. Should people drive while they talk on cell phones?

   _____.

5. Should people talk on cell phones in restaurants?

   _____.

6. Are tests useful?

   _____.

7. Should students be able to take all their college classes online?

   _____.

12g Expressions that Introduce Noun Clauses with *That*

Student Book 2 p. 340, Student Book 2B p. 148

28 **Practice**

Complete the sentences with your own ideas about life and the world. Use a *that* clause and the adjectives from the list.

afraid	furious	sad
amazed	glad	shocked
angry	happy	sure
aware	horrified	surprised
convinced	impressed	terrified
delighted	lucky	thrilled
disappointed	pleased	worried
fortunate	proud	

1. *I'm proud that I lost 30 pounds last year.* (OR)

 I'm not surprised Cindy got a new dog. She loves animals.

2. _____.

3. _____.

4. _____.

5. _____.

6. _____.

7. _____.

8. _____.

9. _____.

10. _____.

11. _____.

12. _____.

13. _____.

14. _____.

15. _____.

16. _____.

17. _____.

18. _____.

19. _____.

20. _____.

21. _____.

22. It's a fact _____.

23. It's true _____.

A   **Choose the best answer, A, B, C, or D, to complete the sentence. Mark your answer by darkening the oval with the same letter.**

1. My mother-in-law loves all flowers. She likes roses, tulips, _____ lilacs.

   A. or   Ⓐ Ⓑ Ⓒ Ⓓ
   B. but
   C. so
   D. and

2. Warren isn't sure if he can come, but he thinks _____.

   A. or   Ⓐ Ⓑ Ⓒ Ⓓ
   B. but
   C. so
   D. and

3. Sherry's not sure which shoes to buy. She likes both pairs, _____ she can't afford both.

   A. or   Ⓐ Ⓑ Ⓒ Ⓓ
   B. but
   C. so
   D. and

4. Brian and Noriko moved to a new town, _____ they don't know many people yet.

   A. or   Ⓐ Ⓑ Ⓒ Ⓓ
   B. but
   C. so
   D. and

5. Hae Jung doesn't like cold weather, and _____ do I.

   A. too   Ⓐ Ⓑ Ⓒ Ⓓ
   B. either
   C. neither
   D. so

6. Sophia's very serious, and _____ is her husband.

   A. too   Ⓐ Ⓑ Ⓒ Ⓓ
   B. either
   C. neither
   D. so

7. Diamonds are expensive, and emeralds are, _____.

   A. too   Ⓐ Ⓑ Ⓒ Ⓓ
   B. either
   C. neither
   D. so

8. We're not sure _____.

   A. was he going   Ⓐ Ⓑ Ⓒ Ⓓ
   B. he was going
   C. where was he going
   D. where he was going

9. I'm not sure _____.

   A. if or not I'll   Ⓐ Ⓑ Ⓒ Ⓓ
      remember to bring the book
   B. what I'll remember to bring the book
   C. whether or not I'll remember to bring the book
   D. to bring the book

10. Rosa thinks we're leaving early, but _____.

    A. I don't think so   Ⓐ Ⓑ Ⓒ Ⓓ
    B. I don't think not
    C. I think so
    D. I think

B **Find the underlined word or phrase, A, B, C, or D, that is incorrect. Mark your answer by darkening the oval with the same letter.**

1. The teachers <u>have to</u> be <u>trained</u> in math,
   A B

   reading, <u>but</u> writing, <u>too</u>.
   C D

   Ⓐ Ⓑ Ⓒ Ⓓ

2. Abdullah <u>doesn't like</u> potatoes, <u>or</u> he
   A B

   ordered a salad. <u>I did</u>, <u>too</u>.
   C D

   Ⓐ Ⓑ Ⓒ Ⓓ

3. <u>The children</u> <u>couldn't</u> <u>go</u> on the field trip.
   A B C

   <u>Either</u> could the teachers.
   D

   Ⓐ Ⓑ Ⓒ Ⓓ

4. I'm not <u>sure</u> what he's thinking <u>but</u> <u>where</u>
   A B C

   <u>he's going</u>.
   D

   Ⓐ Ⓑ Ⓒ Ⓓ

5. Some of the people are wondering

   <u>if or not</u> they <u>should stay</u> <u>or</u> try
   A B C

   <u>to go</u> home.
   D

   Ⓐ Ⓑ Ⓒ Ⓓ

6. We don't know <u>if</u> she's here today <u>or not</u>,
   A B

   <u>but</u> we <u>hope</u>.
   C D

   Ⓐ Ⓑ Ⓒ Ⓓ

7. They were starting <u>to get</u> hungry, <u>but</u>
   A B

   they stopped to eat, <u>and</u> <u>so</u> did we.
   C D

   Ⓐ Ⓑ Ⓒ Ⓓ

8. Clyde was proud <u>that</u> he served in the
   A

   military <u>and</u> <u>either</u> <u>was</u> his family.
   B C D

   Ⓐ Ⓑ Ⓒ Ⓓ

9. Bruce didn't hear the phone <u>and</u> <u>neither</u>
   A B

   did I. Jeannie did, <u>or</u> she answered <u>it</u>.
   C D

   Ⓐ Ⓑ Ⓒ Ⓓ

10. It's <u>supposed</u> to get cold tonight, <u>but</u> I
    A B

    hope <u>not</u>. I really don't like cold
    C

    weather, <u>too</u>.
    D

    Ⓐ Ⓑ Ⓒ Ⓓ

UNIT 13 ADJECTIVE AND ADVERB CLAUSES

13a Adjective Clauses with *Who*, *Whom*, and *That* Referring to People

Student Book 2 p. 346, Student Book 2B p. 154

1 Practice

Underline the adjective clauses in the following paragraph.

The neighbor who lives next door to me wanted to buy my car. Unfortunately, I'd already sold it to a guy who works in my office. The men and women whom I work with are a lot of fun. The department that I work in is quite large and the company that we work for makes electronics. The people who buy our products are very impressed with the quality of our products.

2 Practice

Read the list of mythical (not real) creatures. Complete the sentences by matching the type of creature with the definition.

_____	**1.** A witch is a creature who	**a.** bites people on the neck.
_____	**2.** A fairy is a creature who	**b.** knows magic and rides brooms.
_____	**3.** A werewolf is a creature who	**c.** has died, but we can see him or her.
_____	**4.** A ghost is a creature who	**d.** is very small, has wings, and knows magic.
_____	**5.** A genie is a creature who	**e.** becomes a wolf during a full moon.
_____	**6.** A vampire is a creature who	**f.** lives in a bottle or lamp and answers wishes.

3 Practice

A teacher is talking about some of the students in his class. Combine the sentences with *who*.

1. That student doesn't talk very much in class. He's wearing sandals.

   That student who's wearing sandals doesn't talk very much in class.

2. That student always talks. She has long hair.

   _____.

3. That guy sometimes sleeps. He has an earring.

   _____.

4. The girl is always prepared. She's from New York.

   _____.

5. The boy is from Thailand. He sits next to Cindy.

   _____.

6. The girl never does the homework. She's singing to herself.

   _____.

7. The boy rides his bike to school. He seldom asks questions.

   _____.

8. The boy is the youngest student in the class. He's wearing shorts.

   _____.

4 Practice

Complete the definitions for the following people with *who* or *that*. Use a dictionary if you don't know the word.

1. A composer *is a person who writes music* _____.

2. A ballerina _____.

3. An operator _____.

4. A manicurist _____.

5. A hacker _____.

6. A soldier _____.

7. A veterinarian _____.

8. A spy _____.

9. An acrobat _____.

10. An architect _____.

5 | Practice

Complete the sentences with the appropriate word.

1. _A sculptor_____ is an artist who creates sculptures.

2. _____ is a person who makes people laugh.

3. _____ is a person who cooks professionally.

4. _____ is a person who mixes drinks.

5. _____ is a person who takes care of sick people.

6. _____ is a person who translates languages.

7. _____ is a person who plays poker and goes to casinos.

8. _____ is a person who manages the home, taking care of things

like finances, cleaning, decorating, cooking, or child care.

9. _____ is a person who plays music on the radio.

10. _____ is a person who fixes water pipes in buildings and houses.

6 | Practice

Complete the sentences with your own ideas.

1. The perfect teacher is a person who _knows his/her subject and is able to_

_communicate that knowledge in an interesting way_____.

2. The perfect girlfriend/boyfriend is a person who _____.

3. The perfect friend is a person who _____.

4. The perfect boss is a person who _____.

5. The perfect employee is a person who _____.

6. The perfect coworker is a person who _____.

7. The perfect neighbor is a person who _____.

8. The perfect politician is a person who _____.

9. The perfect athlete is a person who _____.

10. The perfect brother/sister is a person who _____.

13b Adjective Clauses with *That* and *Which* Referring to Things

Student Book 2 p. 350, Student Book 2B p. 158

7 Practice

Joon is studying English clothing vocabulary. Complete the sentences by matching the article of clothing with the definition.

_____ **1.** A scarf is a piece of clothing that

_____ **2.** A belt is a piece of clothing that

_____ **3.** A zipper is something that

_____ **4.** Gloves are pieces of clothing that

_____ **5.** Buttons are things that

_____ **6.** A suit is a piece of clothing that

_____ **7.** Stockings are pieces of clothing that

_____ **8.** A vest is a piece of clothing that

a. consists of a jacket and a skirt or a pair of pants.

b. you wear over your shirt that has no sleeves.

c. you wear on your hands when it is cold.

d. you wear around your neck.

e. keeps your pants up.

f. people wear on their legs when wearing a dress or for extra support.

g. is usually made of metal that connects two pieces of clothing together.

h. are usually round and you put them through holes to connect clothing.

8 Practice

Combine the sentences with *which* or *that*. Sometimes it's a subject pronoun, and sometimes it's an object pronoun.

1. The necklace is on sale. It's made of gold.

   The necklace that/which is on sale is made of gold .

2. The store is open tomorrow. We saw the necklace in it.

   _____.

3. The suitcase fell apart quickly. I bought it there.

   _____.

4. The newspaper is the better one. It's delivered in the morning.

_____.

5. The music is from Egypt. You're listening to it.

_____.

6. The house has been remodeled. It's on the corner.

_____.

7. The CD player has never worked well. It's broken now.

_____.

9 | Practice

A man tried to steal Janelle's purse when she got off the bus last night. Read the following statements. Combine them using _who_ or _which_.

1. The bus was crowded. It comes after 9:00.

   _The bus which comes after 9:00 was crowded_____.

2. The man was big. He attacked me.

_____.

3. The woman helped me. She was on the same bus.

_____.

4. The dog was barking. It tried to bite the man.

_____.

5. The car was red. He jumped into it.

_____.

6. The bag didn't have any money in it. He took it.

_____.

7. The streetlight was burned out. We were under it.

_____.

8. The neighborhood is usually quiet. I live in it.

_____.

9. The man will walk you home, Janelle. He's a police officer.

_____.

10 Practice

Complete the sentences with *that* or *which*.

1. Glasses are things *that help people see* .

2. A computer is a tool _____.

3. A DVD is a plastic disc _____.

4. A jukebox is a machine _____.

5. A castle is a building _____.

6. A remote control is a device _____.

7. A battery is a device _____.

8. Pajamas are clothes _____.

9. A vacuum cleaner is a machine _____.

10. A tattoo is a picture _____.

11 Practice

Read the information on Scotland. Complete the sentences with *who* or *which*.

A kilt is a piece of clothing _____ men
                                      1

sometimes wear in Scotland. Bagpipes are an instrument

_____ is difficult to learn. Loch Ness is a lake
        2

_____ may have an unusual creature living in it.
        3

People _____ live near the lake are a little tired of
           4

all the tourists. English, Gaelic, and Lallans are the languages

_____ are spoken by the people _____
        5   6

live in Scotland.

13c Omission of *Who*, *That*, and *Which*

Student Book 2 p. 352, Student Book 2B p. 160

12 Practice

Read the sentences. Write *C* next to the sentence if the adjective clause is used correctly. Write *I* if it is used incorrectly.

_____ **1.** Francie is the woman I fell in love with in college.

_____ **2.** I met her at a dorm party was held at New Year's.

_____ **3.** She was studying biology was also my major.

_____ **4.** My roommate was from the same hometown Francie was.

_____ **5.** We lived in a room was on the sixth floor of the dorm.

_____ **6.** The classes I went to were always in the afternoon.

_____ **7.** The professors I had were very good.

_____ **8.** After four years, I got a degree was in biology.

_____ **9.** The friends we made in college are still some of our closest ones.

13 Practice

Jake and Diane are talking about their last vacation. Read the sentences. Then rewrite them using adjective clauses, omitting *who, that,* or *which*.

1. These are the photos. We took them last year.

   These are the photos we took last year .

2. This is the camera. Diane used it to take photos.

   _____ .

3. These are the dishes. I bought them in Italy.

   _____ .

4. This is the couple. We met them in the hotel.

   _____ .

5. This is the hotel. We stayed at it.

   _____ .

6. This is the guide. We hired him to take us on a tour of Rome.

   _____ .

7. This is the map. We used it there.

   _____ .

8. This is the car. We rented it while we were there.

   _____ .

9. These are some of the sights. We saw them.

   _____ .

14 Practice

Kent is starting a new job. A coworker is explaining things while Kent is taking notes. Complete the sentences with the relative pronouns *who, that,* or *which*. If the relative pronoun can be omitted, write *X*.

1. This is the desk _____X_____ you'll be using.

2. I'm the person _____ you should see if you have any questions.

3. You'll need to get an ID badge _____ allows you in the building.

4. The phone _____ is on your desk isn't working right now.

5. The department _____ we're in is very busy this time of year.

6. The man _____ is your assistant also works for two other managers.

7. The work _____ we do here is very confidential.

8. The report _____ I'm going to give you needs to be done as soon as possible.

9. The other people _____ are on the floor can also help you if you need it.

13d Adjective Clauses with *Whose*

Student Book 2 p. 353, Student Book 2B p. 161

15 Practice

Underline the correct words in parentheses.

1. The author (whose / who's) book we're reading is working on the next one.

2. I don't really know the people (whose / who's) house we're going to.

3. My friend (whose / who's) usually here wasn't in class today.

4. They gave a promotion to the woman (whose / who's) project was the most successful.

5. The teacher talked to the guy (whose / who's) cell phone rang in class.

6. Shaun doesn't know the man (whose / who's) going to meet him at the airport.

7. The police called the woman (whose / who's) bag was found on the street.

8. The clerk (whose / who's) always so helpful wasn't at the store today.

9. That's the cousin (whose / who's) starting school next fall.

10. The man (whose / who's) house we bought isn't friendly at all.

Use *whose* to join the sentences.

1. The friend is making dinner. We're going to her house.

   The friend whose house we're going to is making dinner .

2. That woman is difficult to work with. I take care of her children.

   _____ .

3. The manager is retiring next year. I admire her intelligence.

   _____ .

4. The professor gave a surprise quiz. We skipped his class.

   _____ .

5. The telecommunications company is going out of business. We're advertising their services.

   _____

   _____ .

6. The neighbor loves parties. We're going to a cookout at his house.

   _____ .

7. We have visited many countries. Their clothing was traditional.

   _____ .

8. The director is making a new movie about rap music. His movies are my favorite.

   _____

   _____ .

9. The passenger was very upset. His wallet was stolen.

   _____ .

10. The team gets a lot of TV coverage. Its players are very popular.

    _____ .

17 Practice

Separate the sentences into two parts.

1. The philosophers whose ideas we're studying lived hundreds of years ago.

    The philosophers lived hundreds of years ago. We're

    studying their ideas.

2. Our classmate whose hobbies include parachuting and dirt biking broke his arm.

    _____

    _____ .

3. The client whose computer crashed hadn't finished working yet.

    _____

    _____ .

4. Our friend whose interview is tomorrow can't sleep.

    _____

    _____ .

5. The woman whose jokes we're laughing at is a lot of fun.

    _____

    _____ .

18 Practice

Complete the conversation with *who's* or *whose*.

Tina: _____ papers are these?
              1

Jerry: I don't know.

Tina: Well, _____ going to pick them up?
                   2

Jerry: _____ turn is it to clean up?
              3

Tina: I think it's Paula's. _____ going to call her?
                                         4

Jerry: I will.

13e Adjective Clauses with Prepositional Phrases

Student Book 2 p. 356, Student Book 2B p. 164

19 Practice

Rewrite the sentences. If the sentence is formal, make it informal. If the sentence is informal, make it formal.

1. A doctor is a person to whom you go if you don't feel well.

   A doctor is a person you go to if you don't feel well .

2. A bad day can be something you're depressed by.

   _____ .

3. A ticket is something for which you pay when you get on the bus.

   _____ .

4. Hobbies are things you're interested in doing in your free time.

   _____ .

5. Tests are things for which students study.

   _____ .

6. Future plans are things we think about when we dream.

   _____ .

20 Practice

First complete the definitions using informal English. Then write the definitions again using formal English. Use phrases from the list.

apologize for	cook with	look forward to	see with
arrested for	depend on	major in	work with
be married to	listen to		

1. Music is something _you listen to_ .

   Music is something to which you listen .

2. A vacation is something _____ .

   _____ .

3. A coworker is someone _____ .

   _____ .

4. A pan is something _____ .

_____ .

5. A crime is something _____ .

_____ .

6. A mistake is something _____ .

_____ .

7. A spouse is someone _____ .

_____ .

_____ .

8. Medicine is something _____ .

_____ .

9. Glasses are something _____ .

_____ .

10. Our friends are people _____ .

_____ .

13f Adverb Clauses with *Because*

Student Book 2 p. 358, Student Book 2B p. 166

|21| **Practice**

Join the sentences with *because* in two different ways. Use correct punctuation.

1. Jay ordered a pizza. He was hungry.

 Jay ordered a pizza because he was hungry .

 Because he was hungry, Jay ordered a pizza .

2. He wanted a better job. He moved to a new town.

_____ .

_____ .

3. He doesn't want his children to watch TV. He doesn't have a TV.

_____ .

_____ .

4. I don't eat meat. I ordered macaroni and cheese.

_____ .

_____ .

5. There's not enough light. My garden isn't doing well.

_____ .

_____ .

6. He's not really happy at his job. He's not doing well.

_____ .

_____ .

7. Mike didn't talk to Maria. He's very shy.

_____ .

_____ .

8. They went to see it two times. They liked it so much.

_____ .

_____ .

9. Bats have excellent hearing. They don't need to see well.

_____ .

_____ .

10. They met on the Internet. They've never seen each other.

_____ .

_____ .

22 ## Practice

Complete the sentences with your own ideas.

1. I'm studying English because _____ .

2. I'm doing this exercise because _____ .

3. I'm (not) going to get married because _____ .

4. Because my parents _____ , I _____ .

5. Because I hate _____ , _____ .

6. I (don't) like scary movies because _____ .

13g Adverb Clauses with *Although* and *Even Though*

Student Book 2 p. 360, Student Book 2B p. 168

23 Practice

Combine the sentences using *although* or *even though*.

1. Randy forgot his grandfather's birthday this year. He's been throwing birthday parties for Johnny, his grandfather, for years.

   Although/Even though Randy's been throwing birthday parties for Johnny, his grandfather, for years, he forgot his birthday this year .

2. Johnny only gardens for fun. He loves plants and working outdoors.

   _____

   _____ .

3. Randy got to the plant store pretty late. It was still open.

   _____

   _____ .

4. He easily found Johnny's favorite white spring flowers. He didn't have much time.

   _____

   _____ .

5. Johnny liked the plants. They were very heavy to carry.

   _____

   _____ .

6. Randy had a busy day planned for Monday. He and Johnny worked all weekend in the garden.

   _____

   _____ .

24 Practice

Combine the sentences using *because, although,* or *even though*.

1. Marlene's a student. She works full time.

   _____

   _____ .

2. She's got lots of homework. She plays volleyball twice a week.

   _____

   _____ .

3. She works. Her parents can't afford to pay for her tuition.

   _____

   _____ .

4. She works 35 hours a week. She gets pretty good grades.

   _____

   _____ .

5. She's taking journalism courses. She wants to announce the news on TV.

   _____

   _____ .

6. She doesn't speak French. She's going to France during spring break.

   _____

   _____ .

7. Her parents are proud of her. She's the first one in her family to go to college.

   _____

   _____ .

8. Her roommates aren't very neat. She likes them a lot.

   _____

   _____ .

25 Practice

Combine the sentences using *because, although,* or *even though*. Try to write one sentence with *although* or *even though* and one with *because*.

1. Clint loves music. He doesn't play an instrument.

   He loves music. He has hundreds of CDs.

   Clint loves music although/even though he doesn't play an instrument.

   Because he loves music, he has hundreds of CDs.

2. My aunt doesn't drive. She knows every street in the city.

   She has lived here for 20 years. She can give anyone directions to her house.

   _____.

   _____.

3. Craig and Louis don't like sports drinks. They usually drink water when they work

   out at the gym.

   Craig likes hot tea. He doesn't like iced tea.

   _____.

   _____.

4. Mark is tall. He doesn't play basketball.

   He's tall. People think he's older than he really is.

   _____.

   _____.

5. Bonnie had a heart attack. Her doctors told her to eat healthier and to start exercising.

   She joined a gym in her neighborhood. She had never been in a gym before.

   She's watching what she's eating. She's losing weight.

   She's never worked out in her life. She's never felt better.

   _____

   _____.

   _____

   _____

   _____.

A **Choose the best answer, A, B, C, or D, to complete the sentence. Mark your answer by darkening the oval with the same letter.**

1. The driver is the man _____ saw the accident.

   A. who   Ⓐ Ⓑ Ⓒ Ⓓ
   B. which
   C. whose
   D. because

2. The snow _____ fell last night isn't enough to ski on.

   A. who   Ⓐ Ⓑ Ⓒ Ⓓ
   B. which
   C. whose
   D. because

3. These are the children _____ parents we met last night.

   A. who   Ⓐ Ⓑ Ⓒ Ⓓ
   B. which
   C. whose
   D. because

4. Brittany didn't sleep well _____ she's worried about a few things.

   A. although   Ⓐ Ⓑ Ⓒ Ⓓ
   B. which
   C. even though
   D. because

5. They kept working _____ the power had gone off.

   A. even though   Ⓐ Ⓑ Ⓒ Ⓓ
   B. which
   C. whose
   D. because

6. The clothes _____ I washed this morning are already dirty again.

   A. who   Ⓐ Ⓑ Ⓒ Ⓓ
   B. which
   C. whose
   D. because

7. We still don't understand _____ the teacher has explained the idea three times.

   A. even though   Ⓐ Ⓑ Ⓒ Ⓓ
   B. which
   C. whose
   D. because

8. He didn't get your message _____ your pager didn't work.

   A. even though   Ⓐ Ⓑ Ⓒ Ⓓ
   B. which
   C. whose
   D. because

9. Jenny doesn't get good grades _____ she tries hard.

   A. even though   Ⓐ Ⓑ Ⓒ Ⓓ
   B. which
   C. whose
   D. because

10. The guests _____ are coming are my husband's friends.

    A. who   Ⓐ Ⓑ Ⓒ Ⓓ
    B. which
    C. whose
    D. because

B **Find the underlined word or phrase, A, B, C, or D, that is incorrect. Mark your answer by darkening the oval with the same letter.**

1. <u>Even</u> <u>though</u> she doesn't like them very
   A   B
   much, Gina has vases <u>who</u> have been
                          C
   in her family <u>for</u> 100 years.
                  D

   Ⓐ Ⓑ Ⓒ Ⓓ

2. The woman <u>who</u> <u>sits</u> next to me <u>was</u> angry
               A   B   C
   <u>although</u> she got a parking ticket.
    D

   Ⓐ Ⓑ Ⓒ Ⓓ

3. Andy's going to see the movie <u>that's</u> at
                                   A
   the cineplex again <u>because</u> he's <u>already</u>
                       B   C
   <u>seen</u> it twice.
    D

   Ⓐ Ⓑ Ⓒ Ⓓ

4. <u>The town</u> <u>who's</u> nearest to ours <u>is</u> in
    A   B   C
   danger <u>because</u> there's a very large fire
           D
   burning.

   Ⓐ Ⓑ Ⓒ Ⓓ

5. <u>Although</u> she owns <u>that</u> nice house <u>which</u>
    A   B   C
   on the corner, she wants to sell it
   <u>because</u> she needs the money.
    D

   Ⓐ Ⓑ Ⓒ Ⓓ

6. The manager <u>who</u> they just hired <u>seems</u>
                A   B
   nice <u>because</u> she's <u>strict</u>.
         C   D

   Ⓐ Ⓑ Ⓒ Ⓓ

7. These are the people <u>who's</u> <u>house</u> we're
                         A   B
   <u>helping</u> to <u>build</u>.
    C   D

   Ⓐ Ⓑ Ⓒ Ⓓ

8. <u>Because</u> it was raining, we <u>went</u> to the
    A   B
   park <u>that</u> <u>is</u> near my house.
         C   D

   Ⓐ Ⓑ Ⓒ Ⓓ

9. This is a town <u>whose</u> <u>residents</u> don't really
                   A   B
   like <u>tourists</u> <u>which</u> come on the weekends
         C   D
   and take all the parking and crowd all
   the stores.

   Ⓐ Ⓑ Ⓒ Ⓓ

10. Your brother <u>can</u> come <u>because</u> I <u>don't</u>
                  A   B   C
    really like him <u>very much</u>.
                     D

   Ⓐ Ⓑ Ⓒ Ⓓ

UNIT 14 REPORTED SPEECH AND CONDITIONAL CLAUSES

14a Quoted Speech

Student Book 2 p. 366, Student Book 2B p. 174

☐1☐ Practice

**Read the jokes. Then rewrite the sentences using quoted speech for the speakers'
words. Use the verb *said* and the correct punctuation.**

1. It was Heather's first airplane trip. She got on the plane and sat in the front seat in
   the front section.

   Man: Excuse me. You're in my seat.
   Heather: Go away. You'll have to find another seat.
   Man: Okay. Fine. You can fly the plane!

   _____ .

   _____ .

   _____ .

2. A bicyclist and a pedestrian crash into each other.

   Bicyclist: Wow. You're really lucky.
   Pedestrian: What do you mean? I'm really hurt!
   Bicyclist: You're lucky because I just lost my license last week. I used to drive a bus!

   _____ .

   _____ .

   _____ .

3. Doctor: What happened to the boy who swallowed the quarter?
   Nurse: There's no change yet.

   _____ .

   _____ .

4. Patient: Doctor, I've lost my memory.
   Doctor: When did this happen?
   Patient: When did what happen?

   _____ .

   _____ .

   _____ .

5. A little boy comes home from school and he's very upset.

    Mother: Ethan, what's wrong?

    Ethan: It's not fair that I can't go into the library with the other kids.

    Mother: Why can't you go to the library?

    Ethan: Because you have to have supervision in order to go in the library, and I wear glasses!

_____ .

_____ .

_____ .

_____ .

14b Reported Speech

Student Book 2 p. 368, Student Book 2B p. 176

2 Practice

Read the following sentences. Write _Q_ next to the sentence if it is quoted speech. Write _R_ if it is reported speech.

A president and a prime minister are discussing a serious situation.

_____ **1.** The president said he was ready to discuss a solution.

_____ **2.** The president said, "I have a couple ideas that can help us."

_____ **3.** The prime minister said that she hadn't seen the president's ideas.

_____ **4.** The prime minister said, "I'll have to speak with the other representatives."

_____ **5.** The president told the prime minister that he understood.

_____ **6.** The prime minister told the president that they had to take care of this soon.

_____ **7.** The president said, "I agree."

_____ **8.** The prime minister said, "I'll call you as soon as I have an answer for you."

_____ **9.** The president said he would be waiting for her call.

Change all the sentences in quoted speech to reported speech.

_____ .

_____ .

_____ .

_____ .

Practice

Read the interview with the famous mystery writer.
Rewrite the writer's answers as reported speech.
Number 1 has two answers.

1. Interviewer: When did you start writing?

   Writer: I knew I wanted to be a writer when I was in high school. During high school, I wrote short stories and worked on the school newspaper.

2. Interviewer: Are you working on any new projects now?

   Writer: I'm writing a new mystery that is set in Brazil.

3. Interviewer: What are your future plans?

   Writer: I have an idea for a new book that will be completely different from what I've always done.

4. Interviewer: How will it be different?

   Writer: It's going to be a historical novel that takes place 200 years ago.

1. _He said he knew he had wanted to be a writer when he was in high school._ _____

2. _____

3. _____

4. _____

Practice

Three students are talking about the homework. Change their quoted speech to reported speech. Make the necessary changes to verbs and pronouns.

1. Dana said, "I don't know what I'm going to write my report on."

   _____

   _____.

2. Horatio said, "I've already finished."

   _____

   _____.

3. Bess said, "I have to work on it tonight."

   _____

   _____.

4. Dana said, "I'm still a little confused."

   _____

   _____.

5. Horatio said, "You should talk to the teacher tomorrow."

   _____

   _____.

6. Bess said, "I did and he really helped me."

   _____

   _____.

7. Dana said, "Okay, I'll speak to him after class."

   _____

   _____.

8. Horatio said, "I'll see you guys tomorrow."

   _____

   _____.

9. Bess said, "I'll walk to the bus stop with you."

   _____

   _____.

5 Practice

Kim and Mick are talking about their friend Dave. Change their underlined reported speech to quoted speech.

1. Mick: <u>Dave told me you already had a boyfriend.</u>

2. Kim: Really? <u>He told me you had a few girlfriends.</u>

3. Mick: <u>He also told me that you didn't have a phone, so I couldn't call you.</u>

4. Kim: <u>He told me you didn't have a job.</u>

5. Mick: I can't believe this! <u>He told me you were busy tomorrow, so I shouldn't ask you out.</u>

6. Kim: What a jerk! <u>He told me he would call me tonight.</u>

7. Mick: He did? <u>He told me he wasn't interested in you.</u>

   Kim: I'm going to call him right now and ask him why he lied to us.

1.   *Dave said, "Kim already has a boyfriend."*

2.   _____

   _____

3.   _____

   _____

4.   _____

   _____

5.   _____

   _____

6.   _____

   _____

7.   _____

   _____

14c *Say* or *Tell*

Student Book 2 p. 372, Student Book 2B p. 180

6 | Practice

Write *C* next to the sentence if the form of *say* or *tell* is used correctly. Write *I* if the form of *say* or *tell* is used incorrectly.

_____ **1.** She didn't say me anything about it.

_____ **2.** Their daughter told the truth.

_____ **3.** Did you get your hair cut? I can't tell the difference.

_____ **4.** What's wrong with Matt? He didn't tell good morning.

_____ **5.** My six-year-old is learning how to say time.

_____ **6.** I'd like to say a few words before I hand back the tests.

_____ **7.** My husband tells our children a story before they go to bed.

_____ **8.** Can you say me the time?

_____ **9.** Don't just sit there! Tell something!

_____ **10.** Adam told me a secret.

7 | Practice

Complete the sentences with *say* or *tell* in the correct tense.

1. My daughter doesn't know how to _____ time. She can't _____ the difference between 1:15 and 1:45. When the teacher calls on her, she doesn't _____ anything.

2. Mom: Did you _____ anything to the boy next door?

     Ray: No, mom.

     Mom: Are you _____ me the truth?

     Ray: Yes, mom!

3. The teacher _____ that we could leave when we're finished. But she also _____ that we had to be sure we'd done a good job. She _____ Bill that she would check it if we wanted her to.

4. Helen's shy. She never _____ good morning.

5. A good movie should _____ a story. I think it

   should _____ something about life.

6. Jim _____ he was going to come right back.

   He _____ me he had to check his parking meter.

7. Wayne: What did Professor Weinberg _____?

   Sarah: She hasn't _____ anything yet.

   Wayne: Are we early? Can you _____ me the time?

   Sarah: Yeah, we have about 10 minutes before class starts.

14d Reported Questions

Student Book 2 p. 374, Student Book 2B p. 182

8 Practice

Before Jim came to Canada to study, his parents asked him a lot of questions. Rewrite their questions as reported speech.

1. Dad asked, "Why do you want to go to Toronto?"

   _____.

2. Mom asked, "Where are you going to live?"

   _____.

3. Dad asked, "Do you know anyone there?"

   _____.

4. Mom asked, "How long are you going to be gone?"

   _____.

5. Dad asked, "Can you get a part-time job there?"

   _____.

6. Mom asked, "Have you gotten a passport yet?"

   _____.

7. Dad asked, "How much is tuition?"

   _____.

8. Mom asked, "Have you been accepted by the university?"

   _____.

Reported Speech and Conditional Clauses

9. Dad asked, "When do you have to buy your ticket?"

_____.

10. Mom asked, "Are you sure this is a good idea?"

_____.

9 Practice

Mrs. McLean, a teacher, is telling a coworker about her student Lewis. Lewis likes to ask a lot of questions in class. Rewrite Lewis's questions as reported speech.

1. "Did we have homework last night?"

Today Lewis asked me _if we had had homework the night before_ .

2. "When's the next test?"

He asked me _____.

3. "May I borrow a pencil?"

He asked me _____.

4. "What was the assignment?"

He asked me _____.

5. "What page are we on?"

He asked me _____.

6. "How do you spell 'assignment'?"

He asked me _____.

7. "When is our next break?"

He asked me _____.

8. "Can I turn in the report tomorrow?"

He asked me _____.

9. "Do I have to finish the exercise now?"

He asked me _____.

10. "Why is English so hard?"

He asked me _____.

10 Practice

Bonnie is looking for a new apartment. Here are the questions she's asking the landlord of a building. Rewrite the questions as reported speech.

1. "Is there a garage?"

   Bonnie asked the landlord _if there was a garage_ .

2. "Do you allow pets?"

   She asked him _____ .

3. "How big is it?"

   She asked him _____ .

4. "When are you showing it?"

   She asked him _____ .

5. "Is the neighborhood quiet?"

   She asked him _____ .

6. "How many rooms does it have?"

   She asked him _____ .

7. "When will it be available?"

   She asked him _____ .

11 Practice

Laura is complaining to her best friend about a terrible job interview. Rewrite the reported questions as quoted questions.

Josie: What happened?

Laura: Well first she wanted to know why I didn't have more experience than I did.
        _____
                                         1
        Then she wanted to know why I'd left my last job. She then wondered if I would
        _____ _____
                       2   3
        work on weekends and until late at night.
        _____
                          3

Josie: It doesn't sound like a very nice place to work.

Laura: She also asked me how much money I made and if I'd work for less money than at
my last job and she inquired if I was good at working with difficult people.

Josie: That doesn't sound good.

Laura: And she wanted to know whether I could start right away.

Josie: What are you going to do?

Laura: I'm going to keep looking.

1. _The interviewer asked, "Why don't you have more
experience than you do?"_

2. _____

_____

3. _____

_____

4. _____

_____

5. _____

_____

6. _____

_____

7. _____

_____

14e Reported Commands, Requests, Advice, and Suggestions

Student Book 2 p. 377, Student Book 2B p. 185

12 Practice

Liz is talking to a friend about her father. Her father is trying to teach her how to drive. Rewrite her dad's "suggestions" as reported speech.

1. "Check your rearview mirror."

First he told me _to check my rearview mirror_ .

2. "Adjust your seat."

_____.

3. "Don't forget to use your turn signal."

_____.

4. "Put on your seat belt."

_____.

5. "Slow down! Don't go so fast."

_____.

6. "Turn left here."

_____.

7. "Turn down that radio, please."

_____.

8. "Keep your hands on the steering wheel."

_____.

9. "Turn on your lights."

_____.

10. "Don't look at me. Look at the road!"

_____.

13 Practice

Complete the sentences with verbs from the list. Use the past tense. In some sentences, there may be more than one correct answer.

advise	ask	invite	order
allow	beg	offer	warn

1. "I'll get the mail," said Michael.

Michael _____ to get the mail.

2. Sarah said, "Please don't smoke in here."

Sarah _____ me not to smoke.

3. Keith said, "You can borrow my car."

Keith _____ me to borrow his car.

4. Jack said, "Would you like to go to a New Year's Eve party with me?"

Jack _____ me to go to a New Year's Eve party with him.

5. Lou yelled, "Stop making all that noise!"

Lou _____ us to stop making noise.

6. Dr. Jang said, "You should get more sleep."

Dr. Jang _____ me to get more sleep.

7. "Please come with us to the party," said Natasha.

Natasha _____ me to come with them to the party.

8. "Don't be late," said the teacher.

My teacher _____ me not to be late.

14 Practice

Complete the sentences with your ideas.

1. Janet's little brother begged her _____.

2. Eman's roommate offered _____.

3. The president allowed_____.

4. The captain ordered _____.

5. The police officer warned _____.

6. The bride and groom invited _____.

7. The voters asked the politicians _____.

15 Practice

Earl has just bought a pet canary. The pet store gave him some rules for taking care of him. Report the rules using *warn, advise, suggest,* or *recommend*.

1. Give him fresh vegetables every day.

   They advised me to give him fresh

   vegetables every day _____.

2. Don't ever give a canary avocado.

   _____.

3. Feed him fresh seed.

   _____.

4. Don't put the cage near the TV.

_____.

5. Make sure he has clean water every day.

_____.

6. Clean his cage often.

_____.

7. Put a toy in his cage.

_____.

16 Practice

Gus has just graduated from college. His friends and family are giving him advice on what he should do next. Rewrite their suggestions two ways using the patterns "suggested/recommended + verb -ing" and "suggested/recommended + subject + base verb."

1. My Aunt Edna said, "You should go on to graduate school."

Aunt Edna recommended I go to graduate school .

She suggested going to graduate school .

2. My dad said, "Why don't you travel?"

_____.

_____.

3. My brother said, "You should look for a good job."

_____.

_____.

4. My sister said, "Don't start working right away!"

_____.

_____.

5. My girlfriend said, "Take some time to think about it."

_____.

_____.

6. My mother said, "Don't worry. Everything will work out."

_____.

_____.

Reported Speech and Conditional Clauses

Practice

Answer the questions.

1. What do you advise tourists to do in your city?

   _____.

2. What do you warn tourists not to do in your city?

   _____.

3. What is something your parents warned you not to do when you were growing up?

   _____.

4. What do you sometimes ask your best friend to do?

   _____.

5. Are teenagers allowed to date in your country? What are some other things teenagers are allowed to do?

   _____

   _____.

14f Wishes about the Present or Future

Student Book 2 p. 381, Student Book 2B p. 189

| 18 | Practice

Write *C* next to the sentence if the wish is correct. Write *I* if the wish is incorrect.

_____ **1.** Junko wishes she were back in Japan now.

_____ **2.** Yoko wishes she is sleeping now.

_____ **3.** Jordan wishes he had a brother.

_____ **4.** I wish I can pass the test.

_____ **5.** Bob wishes his car worked better.

_____ **6.** Becky wishes her computer weren't so slow.

_____ **7.** Ricardo wishes he has a cell phone.

_____ **8.** Deon wishes he could travel more.

_____ **9.** Hazel wishes she speaks Italian.

_____ **10.** I wish I understand English.

19 **Practice**

Ryan would like to make some changes in his life. Here are the things he wishes were different. Write his wishes.

- lives in a cold climate
- doesn't like his job
- doesn't have a pet
- is single
- lives in a big city
- works long hours

1. _Ryan wishes he didn't live in a cold climate._ (OR)

   Ryan wishes he lived in a warm climate.

2. _____.

3. _____.

4. _____.

5. _____.

6. _____.

20 **Practice**

Read the sentences and write wishes from them.

1. Rufus smokes.

   Rufus wishes he didn't smoke .

2. Lillian can't type.

   _____.

3. His son is shy.

   _____.

4. She doesn't make enough money.

   _____.

5. Randy can't swim.

   _____.

6. Allan doesn't drive a nice car.

   _____.

Reported Speech and Conditional Clauses

7. I have to clean my house.

_____.

8. My children don't like the school they go to.

_____.

9. Cheri has a boring job.

_____.

10. I don't like my boss.

_____.

11. Dylan is afraid of horses.

_____.

12. Linda is an only child.

_____.

13. Ron doesn't work out.

_____.

21 Practice

Read the sentences. Write the reality of the situations.

1. I wish I had a million dollars.

Reality: _I don't have a million dollars_____.

2. Karen wishes she were home right now.

Reality: _____.

3. Kyle wishes he knew what he wanted to do when he grows up.

Reality: _____.

4. The children wish they didn't have school tomorrow.

Reality: _____.

5. Cho wishes he spoke Japanese well.

Reality: _____.

6. I wish I could see well without glasses.

   Reality: _____.

7. Jim wishes he'd passed the test.

   Reality: _____.

8. I wish I had a personal trainer.

   Reality: _____.

9. Mike wishes he could sing well.

   Reality: _____.

10. The class wishes it had more time to finish the test.

    Reality: _____.

11. Marcie wishes she had a different job.

    Reality: _____.

12. Larry wishes he liked to drive.

    Reality: _____.

22 Practice

Complete the sentences.

1. I wish I liked _____.

2. I wish I didn't have to _____.

3. I wish I spoke _____.

4. I wish I understood _____.

5. I wish I weren't _____.

6. I wish I lived _____.

7. I wish my job were _____.

8. I wish life were/weren't _____.

9. I wish my computer were _____.

10. I wish my parents had _____.

14g Wishes about the Past

Student Book 2 p. 385, Student Book 2B p. 193

23 Practice

Yesterday was a holiday. I spent it with my family. Write past wishes.

1. I ate too much yesterday.

    I wish I hadn't eaten too much yesterday .

2. I had a fight with my sister.

    _____ .

3. My brother wasn't there.

    _____ .

4. I got there late.

    _____ .

5. I didn't bring anything.

    _____ .

6. I left the presents at home.

    _____ .

7. My girlfriend didn't go with me.

    _____ .

8. It rained all day.

    _____ .

9. I didn't have a good time.

    _____ .

10. I left early.

    _____ .

24 Practice

Read the past wishes. Write the reality.

1. Darla wishes she'd gotten up early.

    Reality: *Darla didn't get up early* .

2. Jeff wishes he'd had some coffee.

Reality: _____.

3. Cary wishes he hadn't left his keys inside.

Reality: _____.

4. Julie wishes she had done the homework.

Reality: _____.

5. The parents wish they'd done things differently.

Reality: _____.

6. My boyfriend and I wish we'd saved more money.

Reality: _____.

7. Dan wishes he'd learned how to play piano.

Reality: _____.

8. Emma wishes she'd bought more bread.

Reality: _____.

25 Practice

Write wishes about Katie's life. Some are in the present and future and some are in the past.

1. Katie doesn't have a job.

Katie wishes she had a job _____.

2. She quit her last one three months ago.

_____.

3. She doesn't have a boyfriend.

_____.

4. She forgot to take her dog Max for a walk this morning.

_____.

5. Her apartment needs painting.

_____.

6. Her car doesn't work.

_____.

7. She cut her own hair last night.

_____.

8. She doesn't feel well.

_____.

9. Her bed is uncomfortable.

_____.

10. She doesn't have any plans next weekend.

_____.

26 Practice

Read the sentences about Jim. Circle if the wish is a present or a past wish.

(present / past)   **1.** Jim wishes he'd learned to play the cello.

(present / past)   **2.** He wishes he'd studied more in school.

(present / past)   **3.** He wishes he weren't so busy.

(present / past)   **4.** He wishes he had more friends.

(present / past)   **5.** He wishes he had traveled more.

(present / past)   **6.** He wishes he had more free time.

(present / past)   **7.** He wishes he had gone to college.

(present / past)   **8.** He wishes he could change his life.

(present / past)   **9.** He wishes he hadn't spent so much time at work.

(present / past)   **10.** He wishes he had some interesting hobbies.

27 Practice

Complete the wishes about the past.

1. I wish I hadn't _____.

2. I wish my parents hadn't _____.

3. I wish they had _____.

4. I wish my teacher had _____.

5. I wish I had _____.

14h Present Real Conditional and Future Conditional Sentences

Student Book 2 p. 387, Student Book 2B p. 195

28 Practice

Write *C* next to the sentence if the real conditional or future conditional is used correctly. Write *I* if it is used incorrectly.

_____ **1.** If we will leave now, we'll be there in 20 minutes.

_____ **2.** The grandchildren won't be hungry later if they eat now.

_____ **3.** The car will work better if we take good care of it.

_____ **4.** You'll be able to use a computer if you will learn how to type.

_____ **5.** Tom will get a better job if he will speak Spanish.

_____ **6.** If they finish it today, they can relax tomorrow.

_____ **7.** If Mary asks me, I'll help.

_____ **8.** If Kristy will go with us, she'll drive.

_____ **9.** We can watch the movie if we have time.

_____ **10.** If you shake cream a long time, it becomes butter.

29 Practice

Don and Claudia are planning a dinner party. Complete the sentences by matching the condition with the result.

_____ **1.** If we invite eight people,

_____ **2.** If we invite Tim,

_____ **3.** Todd won't be able to come

_____ **4.** We can do most of the work Friday night

_____ **5.** If we only serve meat,

a. we'll have to invite his girlfriend.

b. if we have the party on Saturday.

c. we'll need more chairs.

d. Jill won't have anything to eat. She's a vegetarian.

e. if we eat at 8:00.

Reported Speech and Conditional Clauses

Practice

Complete the sentences with the correct form of the verbs in parentheses. Some are present conditionals and some are future conditionals.

1. If Clint (not, start) _____ soon, he (not, finish)

   _____ on time.

2. Jackie (call) _____ us if she (need) _____ help today.

3. If I (not, be) _____ too tired, I (make) _____ a pie later.

4. Sarah (pick) _____ you up if she (take) _____ a taxi.

5. She (can, not, sleep) _____ if she (drink) _____coffee.

6. If Andy and Gene (leave) _____ early, they (miss) _____

   the weekend traffic tonight.

7. If you (lose) _____ your notes, you (can, borrow) _____

   mine.

8. If Anna (work) _____ too hard, she (often, get) _____

   sick.

9. I (be) _____ there at 4:00 if I (leave) _____ now.

10. Darryl (attend) _____ college if he (get) _____ a

    scholarship.

Practice

Complete the sentences with your own ideas.

1. If you mix red and blue, _you get purple_____.

2. If cats like you, they _____.

3. If dogs like you, they _____.

4. If you look directly at the sun, you _____.

5. If you put metal in the microwave, it _____.

6. If you don't water plants, they _____.

7. If fire doesn't have air, it _____.

8. If you drop two objects that have a different weight at the same time, they

   _____.

9. If you put a magnet on metal, it _____.

10. If you eat too much sugar, you _____.

32 Practice

Complete the sentences with *should* or *shouldn't* or write the condition.

1. If you burn your hand, _you should put ice or cold water on it_____.

2. If you have a sore throat, _____.

3. If you get lost in the forest, _____.

4. If you have a car accident, _____.

5. If you have a fever, _____.

6. _____, you should save money.

7. _____, you shouldn't drive.

8. _____, you should learn how to play an instrument.

9. _____, you should travel.

10. _____, you shouldn't answer your cell phone.

33 Practice

Complete sentences about yourself.

1. If I finish this exercise, _____.

2. If I have time tonight, _____.

3. If my family goes on vacation this year, _____.

4. _____ if I get to school late.

5. _____ if I eat too much.

6. _____ if I don't practice.

7. If it rains tonight, _____.

8. If I don't clean my room, _____.

9. _____ if I don't get enough sleep.

10. If I have nightmares, _____.

14i Present Unreal Conditional Sentences

Student Book 2 p. 391, Student Book 2B p. 199

34 Practice

Write *R* next to the sentence if the conditional is real. Write *U* if the conditional is unreal.

_____ **1.** If Ginny has time, she'll meet us later.

_____ **2.** If she didn't have to work, she could come with us.

_____ **3.** If we get enough tomatoes in the garden, I'll give you some.

_____ **4.** If the team goes out for pizza, please call me.

_____ **5.** The park will close if it rains.

_____ **6.** If Cora got up earlier, she wouldn't be late as often.

_____ **7.** Alex would make broccoli if he liked it.

_____ **8.** The class would be happy if they understood conditionals.

_____ **9.** Liz may go back to Canada if she doesn't find a job here.

_____ **10.** Eddie would change if he had clean clothes.

35 Practice

Rewrite the sentences as present unreal conditional sentences.

1. Pigs don't have wings, so they can't fly.

   *If pigs had wings, they could fly*_____.

2. My bed is terrible, so I have back pain.

   _____.

3. Irene doesn't have pets, so she doesn't understand how much responsibility it is.

   _____.

4. Alice studies hard, so she makes good grades.

   _____.

5. His car doesn't have any gas in it, so you have to drive us there.

   _____.

6. My dog doesn't like my brother, so she growled at him.

   _____.

7. Pam doesn't have a phone, so you can't call her.

   _____.

8. Brianna plays tennis every weekend because she likes tennis.

   _____.

9. They can't buy a house because they live in an expensive area.

   _____.

10. Hyung Jung's teachers don't call on her because she's shy.

    _____.

36 Practice

Rewrite the sentences as present unreal conditional sentences.

1. I don't like red. _If I liked red, I'd have that color in my home._

2. Miriam is allergic to cats.

   _____.

3. Hiro doesn't have a camera.

   _____.

4. It's midnight.

   _____.

5. Eileen doesn't read the newspaper.

   _____.

6. It's cold outside.

   _____.

7. Martha doesn't like her homework assignment.

   _____.

8. Seung Wan doesn't cook.

   _____.

9. She doesn't wear makeup.

   _____.

10. You live far away.

    _____.

37 Practice

Read about Carina. Then read the statements. Circle *T* if the statement is true or *F* if the statement is false.

If I had more money, I'd have pretty clothes. I'd be healthier if I didn't like chocolate. If I didn't put off doing things, I'd feel better about myself. I'd take a vacation if I weren't working so much. If I had a car, I could do my grocery shopping more easily. I could play CDs in my car if I had a CD player. If I understood business, I'd open my own restaurant.

T   F   **1.** Carina has nice clothes.

T   F   **2.** She likes chocolate.

T   F   **3.** She puts off doing things.

T   F   **4.** She feels good about herself.

T   F   **5.** She has a car.

T   F   **6.** She's working a lot.

T   F   **7.** She doesn't have a CD player in her car.

T   F   **8.** She understands business.

T   F   **9.** She's going to open her own restaurant.

38 Practice

Complete the sentences with your own ideas.

1. If I had _____, I _____.

2. If I didn't have _____, I _____.

3. I _____ if I were _____.

4. I _____ if I weren't _____.

5. If I were stronger, _____.

6. I _____ if I didn't have to _____.

7. If there were peace all over the world, _____.

8. I _____ if I found a wallet.

9. If I could change one thing in my life, _____.

10. If I didn't have to finish this exercise, _____.

14j Past Unreal Conditional Sentences

Student Book 2 p. 394, Student Book 2B p. 202

39 Practice

Read about Todd's good day yesterday. Rewrite the sentences as past unreal conditional sentences.

1. I missed my bus, so I had to walk, and I found some money on the street.

   If I hadn't missed my bus, I wouldn't have found money on the street .

2. I found the money, so I was able to buy coffee for the woman I met at the coffee shop.

   _____ .

3. We walked to the bus stop together, so we got to know each other.

   _____ .

4. She gave me her phone number, so I called her and asked her to go out.

   _____ .

5. She said yes, so I made reservations at my favorite restaurant.

   _____ .

6. We enjoyed dinner, so we decided to go to a movie.

   _____ .

7. We had a lot to talk about, so we had a good time.

   _____ .

40 Practice

Complete the sentences by matching the cause with the result. Some of them are past unreal conditional sentences and some are present unreal conditional sentences.

_____ 1. If we had had email when I was 20,

_____ 2. If the server hadn't dropped the soup,

_____ 3. If the show were funnier,

_____ 4. If the power hadn't gone out,

_____ 5. If Matt liked me,

_____ 6. If Jessie hadn't been so tired,

a. his customers wouldn't have gotten burned.

b. we could have had the party at our house.

c. I'd ask him for help.

d. she wouldn't have slept on the train and missed her stop.

e. I could have written to my family when I lived in China.

f. I wouldn't be bored.

41

Practice

Read about José's car accident. Then read the statements. Circle _T_ if the statement is true or _F_ if the statement is false.

If José hadn't needed something at the store, he wouldn't have gone to the grocery store. If it hadn't been so foggy, José would have seen the stop sign. If he'd seen the stop sign, he wouldn't have hit the truck. If he hadn't hit the truck, he wouldn't have had to go to the hospital. If he hadn't gone to the hospital, he could have died.

T   F   **1.** José didn't need anything at the store.

T   F   **2.** It was foggy that night.

T   F   **3.** José saw the stop sign.

T   F   **4.** He didn't hit the truck.

T   F   **5.** He didn't go to the hospital.

T   F   **6.** He died.

42

Practice

Read conditional sentences about Alexander Fleming, the discoverer of penicillin. Then write the reality.

If Alexander Fleming hadn't left bread in a petri dish, he wouldn't have seen mold growing on the old bread. If he hadn't looked at the mold, he wouldn't have seen that the mold killed the bacteria. If he hadn't seen the dead bacteria, he wouldn't have discovered penicillin. If Alexander Fleming hadn't discovered penicillin, millions of people could have died from infections.

1. _Alexander Fleming left bread in a petri dish, so he saw mold on the old bread_.

2. _____

_____.

3. _____

_____.

4. _____

_____.

43 Practice

Read the sentences as past unreal conditional sentences. Then write the reality.

1. If Jonathan had come straight home, he wouldn't have gotten into trouble.

   Reality: _____

   _____.

2. The children could have stayed longer if they'd gotten permission.

   Reality: _____

   _____.

3. The ambulance wouldn't have made it to the hospital if it hadn't turned on the siren.

   Reality: _____

   _____.

4. If Toni hadn't eaten so much before dinner, she would have had some dessert.

   Reality: _____

   _____.

5. If I'd been angry, you would have known it.

   Reality: _____

   _____.

6. If Jerry had been nicer to his neighbor, his neighbor wouldn't have been rude.

   Reality: _____

   _____.

44 Practice

Complete the sentences with your own ideas.

1. If humans hadn't gone to the moon, _____.

2. If my parents hadn't met, _____.

3. If my country had _____, it _____.

4. If I hadn't learned how to read, _____.

5. If I hadn't _____, I would have _____.

6. If I had _____, I wouldn't have _____.

Reported Speech and Conditional Clauses

SELF-TEST

A **Choose the best answer, A, B, C, or D, to complete the sentence. Mark your answer by darkening the oval with the same letter.**

1. Sam told me he _____ the project.

   A. finish   Ⓐ Ⓑ Ⓒ Ⓓ
   B. had finished
   C. finishes
   D. would finished

2. Darren asked Lisa _____ she wanted for her birthday.

   A. if   Ⓐ Ⓑ Ⓒ Ⓓ
   B. that
   C. whether
   D. what

3. Ms. Andrews asked her assistant _____ he could work late.

   A. if   Ⓐ Ⓑ Ⓒ Ⓓ
   B. that
   C. when
   D. what

4. Dr. Jenkins said she _____ everyone.

   A. would call   Ⓐ Ⓑ Ⓒ Ⓓ
   B. call
   C. will called
   D. would

5. The class begged their teacher _____ them anymore homework.

   A. gave   Ⓐ Ⓑ Ⓒ Ⓓ
   B. didn't give
   C. to give
   D. not to give

6. Tina wishes she _____ home now.

   A. had been   Ⓐ Ⓑ Ⓒ Ⓓ
   B. is
   C. isn't
   D. were

7. Yoko wishes she _____ up earlier.

   A. get   Ⓐ Ⓑ Ⓒ Ⓓ
   B. had gotten
   C. gets
   D. have gotten

8. If I don't sleep late, I _____ you for coffee.

   A. joined   Ⓐ Ⓑ Ⓒ Ⓓ
   B. join
   C. will join
   D. would join

9. If we didn't advertise, we _____ as successful as we are.

   A. wouldn't be   Ⓐ Ⓑ Ⓒ Ⓓ
   B. would have
   C. aren't
   D. hadn't been

10. If it _____ last summer, our farm would have been in trouble.

    A. rained   Ⓐ Ⓑ Ⓒ Ⓓ
    B. didn't rain
    C. will rain
    D. hadn't rained

B   **Find the underlined word or phrase, A, B, C, or D, that is incorrect. Mark your answer by darkening the oval with the same letter.**

1. Aunt Mary <u>says</u> she would <u>do</u> it <u>when</u> we
   　　　　　 A　　　　　　　 B　　　 C

   <u>got</u> home later.
   　D

   Ⓐ Ⓑ Ⓒ Ⓓ

2. The counselor <u>wanted</u> <u>to know</u> <u>that</u> our
   　　　　　　　　 A　　　 B　　 C

   parents <u>did</u> for a living.
   　　　　 D

   Ⓐ Ⓑ Ⓒ Ⓓ

3. Fran <u>suggested</u> <u>to</u> <u>leaving</u> early, but no
   　　　 A　　　　 B　 C

   one <u>listened</u> to her.
   　　 D

   Ⓐ Ⓑ Ⓒ Ⓓ

4. If you <u>had</u> <u>listened</u> to me, you <u>would</u>
   　　　　 A　　 B　　　　　　　 C

   have <u>did</u> it correctly the first time.
   　　　 D

   Ⓐ Ⓑ Ⓒ Ⓓ

5. They <u>wanted</u> to know <u>when</u> we <u>were</u>
   　　　 A　　　　　　　 B　　　 C

   <u>going</u> to be late.
   　D

   Ⓐ Ⓑ Ⓒ Ⓓ

6. My dad <u>wishes</u> he <u>is</u> younger than he is.
   　　　　 A　　　　 B

   If he <u>were</u>, he'<u>d run</u> every morning.
   　　　 C　　　 D

   Ⓐ Ⓑ Ⓒ Ⓓ

7. Donna <u>would</u> have <u>bought</u> the car <u>if</u> she
   　　　　 A　　　　 B　　　　　 C

   <u>has</u> enough money.
   　D

   Ⓐ Ⓑ Ⓒ Ⓓ

8. If Will hadn't already <u>saw</u> the movie, he
   　　　　　　　　　　 A

   <u>would</u> <u>have</u> <u>come</u> with us.
   　B　　 C　　 D

   Ⓐ Ⓑ Ⓒ Ⓓ

9. Cindy <u>wish</u> she <u>hadn't</u> <u>gotten</u> <u>so</u> angry.
   　　　 A　　　 B　　 C　　 D

   Ⓐ Ⓑ Ⓒ Ⓓ

10. Gail <u>advised</u> the parents <u>not</u> <u>get</u> upset
    　　　 A　　　　　　　　 B　 C

    and <u>to try</u> talking more.
    　　 D

    Ⓐ Ⓑ Ⓒ Ⓓ

Reported Speech and Conditional Clauses